H. S. Pepoon
PIONEER CONSERVATIONIST OF NORTHWEST ILLINOIS
Essays on Ecology 1904-1933

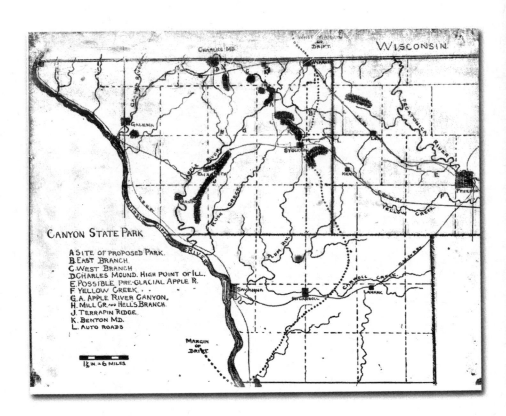

CANYON STATE PARK

A SITE OF PROPOSED PARK.
B EAST BRANCH.
C WEST BRANCH.
D CHARLES MOUND. HIGH POINT OF ILL.
E POSSIBLE PRE-GLACIAL APPLE R.
F YELLOW CREEK.
G A. APPLE RIVER CANYON.
H MILL GR. AND HELL'S BRANCH.
J TERRAPIN RIDGE.
K BENTON MD.
L AUTO ROADS

1½ IN. = 6 MILES

H.S. PEPOON

PIONEER CONSERVATIONIST OF NORTHWEST ILLINOIS

Essays on Ecology 1904-1933

COMPILED and *PUBLISHED* by:

CORY RITTERBUSCH

Head Restoration Ecologist & Historian,
Prairie Works, Inc.

with ALL ORIGINAL

MAPS & PHOTOGRAPHS

FOREWORD BY: WILLIAM HANDEL

BOTANIST ILLINOIS NATURAL HISTORY SURVEY

WITH AN EXTENSIVE INTRO-
DUCTION by the PUBLISHER.

PRAIRIEWORKS

GALENA, ILLINOIS

2011

Printed by Union-Hoermann Press
Dubuque, Iowa
U.S.A.

Cover Photo: Color Lantern Slide of Bird's Eye Primrose: Lantern Slide Box Number, 2, Slide number 30, Herman Silas Pepoon Papers, Chicago Academy of Sciences.

Opposite Title Page: Lantern Slide (Line Drawing) of Northwest Illinois: Lantern Slide Box Number, 1, Slide number 22, Herman Silas Pepoon Papers, Chicago Academy of Sciences.

Book Design: Cory Ritterbusch and Arrasimages.com, Galena, Ill.

ISBN 978-0-615-43123-9
E-book 978-0-615-50682-1

First Edition, June 2011
Second Printing, October 2011

P.O. Box 6623
Galena, Ill. 61036

CONTENTS.

PREFACE.

THE FIRST TIME I came across the name H. S. Pepoon was in 1999. I was reading *The Driftless Area: an Inventory of the Region's Resources* published by the Illinois Department of Natural Resources the previous year. The report highlighted Pepoon's discovery of the Bird's Eye Primrose plant at Apple River Canyon State Park. In 2003, his name came up again, in reference to his *An Annotated Flora of the Chicago Region*, published in 1927. Several peers lauded this work as groundbreaking, and the precursor to the familiar *Plants of the Chicago Region* first published in 1969.

In 2006, now living in and restoring the ecosystems of Northwest Illinois, I had my next encounter with H. S. Pepoon. His *An Ecological Survey of the Driftless Area* was cited during research of the sand prairie at the Savanna Army Depot. The title of the paper attracted me enough to spend thirty dollars for a digital copy, which I downloaded to my computer. Through this method, I slowly began to assemble more of his work, and, like a detective, followed a lead from one search result to another. After locating a complete Pepoon work (which often took weeks), I would convert it to a portable document format (.pdf) file. With each new paper discovered, I became more entrenched, for I was gaining wonderfully detailed descriptions of the local land written by a botanist 100 years prior. I also grew curious about the author himself, especially after learning he was from Northwest Illinois. Pepoon, in fact, grew up just fifteen miles from my house. Over the next three years, I visited many of our local libraries and made several trips to Chicago for research. The information compiled was like a found treasure to me. I began to revere Herman Pepoon, perhaps more so than my longtime environmental icon, Aldo Leopold. I began speaking of Pepoon to many, with

i

much enthusiasm. Eventually it was suggested that these papers be consolidated into a collection for public appreciation and to raise awareness of a person important to the region. The timing of this book, coincidentally, would honor Pepoon around the 150th anniversary of his birth.

A few items to note:

1- Considerable information has purposely been omitted, including how modern floristic surveys compare to Pepoon's sampling. Some localities and personal information not pertinent to Pepoon's work and life in Northwest Illinois have also been omitted.

2- The faux pattern found on the cover is from a 1920's era composition notebook from my personal collection. The photo is of the Bird's Eye Primrose plant at Apple River Canyon. This was taken between 1910 and 1917 and presumably hand-colored by a lantern slide colorist at the time. It was found in the Pepoon collection at the Chicago Academy of Sciences and would have been used by Pepoon for presentation purposes using a "magic lantern machine." It was scanned at 800 d.p.i resolution into a tagged image file format (.tiff), for use here.

3- Many of the botanical names in the papers have been changed since Pepoon's time, as taxonomists felt the need to reclassify certain plants. This is also very true with common names, many of which would have been regional slang.

4- The writings and photographs have largely been left intact. It was decided that any roughness in the prints should remain, to retain historical integrity.

5- The title page and all book design facets, including typesetting, emulate Pepoon's 1927 book *Flora of the Chicago Area* and other books of that era.

6- *The Chicago Manual of Style* was used to cite references, as was common in books printed in the Middle West that dealt with natural history.

Acknowledgments

I would like to thank those who inspired this collection and made its publication possible:

Foremost, Richard B. Pearce, who diligently provided the book's design and graphic arts work, not allowing for procrastination. His knowledge of botany, historical writing and technology made him the most valuable asset to the project. To Christine Giannoni at The Chicago Field Museum, who worked so efficiently to retrieve archives. Amber King and the Chicago Academy of Sciences, for her optimism and the many important details uncovered. The Illinois State Academy of Science; their permission to reprint many of the papers made this project ultimately possible. Chris Bennett, long-time *kamerad* who generously provided his editing services. The internet search engine Google, a sometimes stubborn mule which, with enough coercion, would eventually take me where I needed to go. Finally, to my wife, family and clients, who allow me to maintain the occupation that I love.

— Cory J. Ritterbusch, February 2011

FOREWORD.

ON ANY GIVEN DAY, if you listen in on conversations of naturalists, botanists, or ecologists, you will hear a common mantra repeated: "If only we had a time machine to transport us back for a week or a day, to see what the landscape was like before it all changed." Not a day has gone by while doing fieldwork that I have not fantasized about being transported back in time to understand the chain of events that would explain a plant community or a unique assemblage of flora or fauna. Fortunately, for people who study the natural world, there sometimes comes along a rare individual whose devotion, dedication and unrelenting quest for knowledge gives us that window in time. Herman Silas Pepoon was such a person, and his years of study provides us with numerous clues to the puzzle. His written observations help us better understand what we observe in the present.

From the 1870's to the late 1930's, Pepoon studied plants throughout Illinois and other states, though always returning to the area around his boyhood home in eastern Jo Daviess County. The land known as the "Driftless Area" was his laboratory and during his extensive "trampings," he gathered invaluable data on the plants, plant communities and other natural history of this unique area of Illinois.

Like Pepoon, I was raised on a farm in the Driftless Area adjacent to land that would later become one of our state parks. Although I often hiked the Mississippi Palisades State Park in my youth, I did not fully appreciate the ecological significance of the area until many years later. After college, I was fortunate to conduct a botanical study of the park. It is during this time, while looking at *A floristic study of Apple River Canyon State Park in the Wisconsin Driftless Division* by Jim Heim (1984) and *Vascular flora of the*

v

Mississippi Palisades Park by Richard Wunderlin (1965), that I became acquainted with Pepoon's works on the natural history of the Driftless Area.

Pepoon is probably best known for his extensive work on cliff communities and his discovery of the rare *Primula mistassinica* (Bird's Eye Primrose) in Apple River Canyon State Park. His discovery of numerous rare species, too extensive to mention here, and his description of plant communities, are invaluable. It was his devotion to detail and intensive study that led to the protection of Apple River Canyon and later the Mississippi Palisades State Park. Pepoon had a unique perspective and natural ability to bring together the scientific fields of hydrology, soils, geography, geology and what we now refer to as "succession" into his study of the plant communities in the Driftless Area. Throughout many of Pepoon's writings, he refers to the depletion of the water table due to deforestation, and erosion due to cultivation of the steep terrain. Pepoon realized early in his life the effect that this would have on the cliff and forest communities on and near his family farm and throughout the Driftless Area.

He conducted his studies during an era that provided an interesting overview of the natural landscape. Some virgin stands of forest and prairie remained and Pepoon provided us with valuable information on species composition. Because of the mining near Galena, Northwest Illinois was one of the first areas to be settled in the 1820's. During Pepoon's time, many plant communities were in a period of regrowth. In my opinion, Pepoon's descriptions of these communities and plant associations are uniquely important. For example, in his work *The Forest Associations of Northwestern Illinois*, he describes the flora of the *aspen-poplar* association. He mentions two species that are very rare in the state today, *Tomanthera auriculata* (auriculate false foxglove) and *Coeloglossum viride* (bracted green orchid), occurring exclusively in this particular community type. As botanists, we often overlook these early successional communities as a source of ecological importance, forgetting that some unique native species thrive in these transitional areas. Since reading Pepoon's work, I have spent more time looking at these areas. Although the above-mentioned species have not been located since Pepoon's time, other interesting species that are rare or lacking in other community types in the Driftless Area have been found.

For me, one of Pepoon's most interesting works is *The Flora of the Right of Way of the Illinois Central Railway*. Pepoon traveled the Galena River Valley from East Dubuque to Scales Mound, Illinois and identified some 605 species of plants. I was able to retrace Pepoon's steps in 2000 and 2001 during my own botanical survey of the area. Exploring the Galena River Valley seventy odd years after Pepoon was one of the high points of my botanical career. Obviously, times had changed; the vast prairie vegetation that he described was mostly gone. The forest communities and wetlands were also absent or degraded. However, using Pepoon's description and detailed localities, I found some of the same uncommon species still occurring in the Galena River Valley. I found *Valeriana edulis ciliata* (edible valerian), a plant unrecorded in the Driftless Area of Illinois at that time. It was on a hill prairie remnant under red cedar trees. This was peculiar because this plant occurs almost exclusively in wetland habitats such as fens or sedge meadows more than 50 miles east of Jo Daviess County. Pepoon mentioned this plant in this valley during his trek to Scales Mound. I wondered if Pepoon had found this very population of valerian. Pepoon mentioned in his writings the influence of native peoples and their effect on the flora and its distribution. Did he wonder how this plant got to such an unlikely place? Had native people transported the seed here in a medicine or food bag and somehow it survived the long years after they themselves vanished?

Cory Ritterbusch has gathered all the rare writings of Herman S. Pepoon on the Driftless Area, and he provides us with background on this unique individual. While reading Pepoon's writings in preparation for this foreword, some for the first time, I was reminded of something in particular I enjoy about his writing. While I appreciate his scientific discoveries and the information he provided future generations of naturalists, I must say that I really admire the spiritual connection he had with the land. Pepoon witnessed the destruction of many of the areas he cherished. Yet it seems to me the thrill of a new plant discovery or a day in the field was just as enjoyable to him at the end of his life as it was when he was a boy counting the showy lady-slipper orchids on his family farm.   His contribution to understanding the land we call the Driftless Area lives on today in his plant collections, historic writings, and protected land.   We might not have that time machine, but we do have the writings of Herman S. Pepoon.

— William C. Handel, Illinois Natural History Survey

INTRODUCTION.

THE WRITTEN COLLECTION CONTAINED herein allows rare accessibility to environmental papers that will intrigue a variety of people and foster appreciation for its writer. These writings from the early 1900's offer both technical and simple descriptions of the flora and terrain in Northwest Illinois as it was then, written by a native son with a powerful conservation voice. This is a snapshot of time taken by one of the country's leading botanists who called Jo Daviess County home: Dr. Herman Silas (H. S.) Pepoon.

Jo Daviess County, which lies in the northwest corner of Illinois, has long been a haven for outdoorsmen, historians, artists, nature lovers and, most recently, environmentalists. H. S. Pepoon was the first professional botanist to study its natural areas, write with authority on its flora and changing land use, analyze its open spaces and express displeasure with ecosystem abuses. He was among the first to promote the great attributes of the area to those who live elsewhere, creating the vision of a tourism industry that flourishes in Jo Daviess County today. The reader of these papers will find the most detailed pre-World War II (and possibly until the 1990's) land descriptions of Northwest Illinois. These writings can be a refreshing discovery for those who restore ecosystems in the Upper Midwest, enjoy natural areas, appreciate local history, read primary source documents or find interest in the evolution of environmental ethics. Curious novice botanists, with a sense of wonder like Pepoon's, should find this book especially engaging.

Ecologists who study the science of restoration ecology often look for historical information to describe former land conditions, mainly in respect to its flora. Traditionally, the most popular resources are land surveyor notes from the 1820's to 1840's, artist renderings, pioneer settler diaries, turn of the century photographs and aerial photographs from the 1940's. Although very useful and important, the practitioners of these media were not botanists. As a result, ecologists using these sources often must make assumptions regarding plant species or ecosystem type. This is not the case with Pepoon's work; he cites specific plants and, in some cases, draws maps to show exact plant locations. Especially important is the timing of his writings, which stands at the transition between the pre-settlement era, with its pristine, virgin natural areas, and the industrial era, characterized by urbanization, degradation and the introduction of non-native weed species. On his frequent trips back home to Northwest Illinois from Chicago, Pepoon documents both the land of the Native American and the land of the industrial future. He recounts images from the previous generation to offer a timeline of land use change up to that point. In *The Forest Lands of Jo Daviess County* (1920), for example, he writes:

> The writer is informed by old settlers that in
> those days there was very little underbrush
> except in moist places, and that one could ride
> in any direction through the timber without
> difficulty.

The following papers presented in this book address the flora and ecology of Northwest Illinois, specifically in Jo Daviess County: *Destruction of a Farm Flora* (1904), *Cliff Flora of Jo Daviess County* (1909), *An Ecological Survey of the Driftless Area of Illinois and Wisconsin* (1909), *The Forest Associations of Northwestern Illinois* (1910), *Peculiar Plant Distributions* (1916), *The Primrose Rocks of Illinois* (1917), *A Proposed New State Park* (1919), *The Forest Lands of Jo Daviess County* (1920), *The Apple River Canyon of Jo Daviess County–A Proposed State Park* (1921), *The Flora of the Rights of Way of the Illinois Central Railway: Waddams to East Dubuque* (1927) and *Primula mistassinica in Illinois and in Distribution* (1933).

A Guide to the Papers

Brief background information for each included paper is shared below to introduce the reader to the content.

Destruction of a Farm Flora (1904)

This paper was originally published in *The Plant World,* a monthly journal of popular botany, official publication of The Wild Flower Preservation Society of America. Pepoon starts the short essay, and this book, with a clear and enthusiastic endorsement of native plant protection. He describes the "destruction" of plant life on his home farm near Warren, drawing from both personal memory and his journals. His sketched maps assist in clarifying this destruction. One can chuckle as he calls weedy plants "plebeians" and "tramps." It is interesting to note that in 1876, at the age of fifteen, he listed 355 plants growing on his home farm. His plant identification skills were certainly advanced for his age, showing a passion for his native flora that he never abandoned. The paper concludes: "I fear (for) all forest plants, for man seems determined to clear the earth of trees of natural growth, leaving it bare and desolate under the fierce heat of our summer sun."

The Cliff Flora of Jo Daviess County (1909)

This is the first of eight papers written for the Illinois State Academy of Science. It includes a general description of Jo Daviess County and details of the plant life on the county's rock features. Although the title would seemingly represent cliffs with vertical slopes, the average limestone outcropping is studied extensively and his observations still apply today. Pepoon expresses frustration with land use practices: "These rough, untillable, non-pasturable, and largely *untreadable* slopes, have, however a very great influence on the plant life of the region (...) for the last stand against a *civilized* death-warrant." He states that because of the steep and jagged rock, cattle are unable to feast on the plant life in these areas, allowing the ecosystem to remain intact. He closes the paper with somewhat startling but useful words of caution for the budding botanist:

> It might be noted that the seeker after plant
> knowledge on these precarious rocky heights
> may on occasion be stopping to admire the
> brazen beauty of the poison ivy or wonder at the
> innocent immaculate appearance of the deadly

Amanita and meet (with a back bone chill) the
unwinking glare of a huge timber-rattlesnake
and stepping backward to avoid the triple danger,
plunge downward a hundred feet to the cold
river beneath.

An Ecological Survey of the Driftless Area of Illinois and Wisconsin [Parts One and Two] (1909)

This two-part paper, written for the *School Science and Mathematics Association Journal*, leaves much to be desired.   The title would have been better if changed from "Driftless Area" to "Jo Daviess County," as the paper focuses on the Jo Daviess County, Illinois, portion of the much larger Driftless Area.   Yet the topic is still too broad for Pepoon's format.   He writes that the purpose of the paper is to manifest his "zeal for botanical collections" from the area of his youth.   Unfortunately, he touches on many subjects only vaguely and, in closing, claims the topic "inadequately treated."   He indicates plans to complete a more exhaustive survey in the future and mentions the "full merits" will go to the Missouri Botanical Gardens (research indicates this did not happen.)   Of note in part two of the survey is Pepoon's accurate explanation of how the flora in the Driftless Area is distinctly different than in the adjacent flat terrain, and his description of the forces that cause the differences.

The Forest Associations of Northwest Illinois (1910)

Here, Pepoon analyzes the forest types in Jo Daviess County and how they associate with soils, hydrology and aspect (slope direction).   He breaks the county into seven separate forest types and analyzes each one, adding information on the shrub understory and herbaceous ground level.   Three important topics emerge: buffalo wallows, Indian-set fires and Bur Oak openings.   Buffalo wallows persisted long after the disappearance of the buffalo, some 100 years earlier, and were still common as late as the 1890's.   Native Americans deliberately ignited prairie fires and left an impact on the land long after their removal.   He notes that with the coming of the Whites there was a cessation of these fires, a reality we still feel the impact of today.   His description of

Bur Oak openings leaves him with unanswered questions on what forces caused this ecosystem. He describes a typical Midwest oak savanna, a rare ecosystem today. He finishes the paper by listing 67 woody species occurring in Jo Daviess County, a list that could now be used as a native planting guide. This paper contains highly relevant information for people interested in ecological restoration in the Upper Midwest.

Peculiar Plant Distributions (1916)

This paper is a great testament to the amount of botanizing done by Pepoon up to this point. He counts 2,500 square miles being "carefully explored," walking (or what he calls "tramping") 1,000 miles and examining thousands of individual plants over the past 40 years. This paper describes the rarest of the plants he encountered in Fulton County (where he lived in the 1880's), the Chicagoland area and Jo Daviess County. I think of this paper as his tramping Hall of Fame, an opportunity to showcase his greatest findings. His closing is a valuable statement explaining the reasons that led to these plants existing in their respective locations.

The Primrose Rocks of Illinois (1917)

Pepoon devotes this paper to describe Bird's Eye Primrose (*Primula mistassinica*), discovered in April 1905, the signature plant discovery of Pepoon's career. He describes its habits, associations and even predicts its future safety. Global warming was not an issue at this time and probably a threat that he could not fathom. Today, this plant serves as a barometer of global warming, as it is a boreal plant currently surviving in non-boreal Jo Daviess County. Bird's Eye Primrose is the trophy plant of Apple River Canyon State Park, which undoubtedly led to its creation as a state park.

A Proposed New State Park (1919)

A diversion from the scientific styling of previous papers, Pepoon writes with great passion to make the case for protecting his boyhood stomping grounds for all to enjoy. Pepoon's leadership skills shine in this masterfully written persuasive paper which, by all accounts, worked.   His vision of the future is spot-on:

> It is earnestly urged that all who can visit this
> region, and learn at first hand what it has to
> offer of beauty and wildness, recreation and
> rehabiliment for all the care-worn, business
> fagged, mentally benumbed citizens of our great
> commonwealth, who here may come to renew
> themselves with might in the inner and outer man.

Some fifty years later the first resort community was planned eight miles west of the park.   Today, Jo Daviess County is a popular destination for weekend getaways and vacation homes—dare we say, for the "business fagged" who "come to renew themselves."   This is H. S. Pepoon inspiring a vision, one he saw before many others.

The Forest Lands of Jo Daviess County (1920)

This paper includes the most accurate data to document land use change in Jo Daviess County.   The four well-detailed, nicely drawn sketch maps, along with the accompanying commentary, present an accurate document for current land use comparison.   Pepoon estimates that 64,000 acres in the county are untillable and also discusses abandoned lead mine shafts and the spoils (excavated soil) taken from them as "better than manure."   Pepoon's work here on soil types predated what was done by the Illinois Cooperative Soil Survey by eight years.   Unlike previous papers, a comprehensive conclusion is included, as standard in scientific papers today.

The Apple River Canyon of Jo Daviess County (1921)

This paper was written for the group The Friends of Our Native Landscape, founded by Jens Jensen in 1913.   The goal of the group was to legally protect important natural areas in Illinois.   In 1921 they published *Proposed Park Areas in the State of Illinois—A Report with Recommendations* for presentation to the state legislature.   The first chapter in the book was Pepoon's description of Apple River Canyon.   This is similar to *A Proposed State Park* from two years earlier, but intended for a more specific audience.

The Flora of the Rights of Way of the Illinois Central Railway: Waddams to East Dubuque (1927)

This is his final paper, written at 67 years of age, as he was also writing his book, *An Annotated Flora of Chicago.* The detailed list of plants and the statistics in this study make for interesting modern comparison. For instance, it is well known that railroad rights-of-way are still some of the best places to find native plants. Pepoon explains the railroad's relationship with plant life in great detail early in the paper and finishes by writing, "The railroad possesses the last rear guard of the innumerable host of beauties that once made glad the Illinois lands." Critical of the rail industry's inattention to the landscape, he calls it a "soulless corporation." The call for protection of railroad rights-of-way continues today and efforts to work with railroad companies remain frustrating.

Primula mistassinica in Illinois and in Distribution (1933)

This completed short paper was never officially published. It was written while Pepoon was working for the Illinois Natural History Survey. He revisits his premier plant that he discovered 25 years earlier and proves its rarity on a continental scale. Pepoon uses maps to show locations of *Primula mistassinica* worldwide and describes its scattered populations. One realizes the odd distinction of this plant's presence in Jo Daviess County, Illinois. In his conclusion, Pepoon gives thanks to Norman Fassett, linking Pepoon to one of the great pioneer conservationists from Wisconsin. Diligently researched, this paper shows Pepoon's passion enduring at the age of 74.

The "Scrapbook"

During the research of this book countless Pepoon artifacts were discovered. A "scrapbook" section is included to showcase unique miscellaneous documents related to Pepoon's life and work. These include newspaper clippings, field notes, pictures and sketches. These materials provide insight into Pepoon's craft and show off his diverse knowledge base, while adding historical perspective. Artifacts included papers on edible plants, such as fruits and vegetables, and non-plant life, such as fish, birds and insects. These reveal passions for the natural world even beyond what is evident in his published work and his sketches of birds and fish reveal an artistic talent unknown previously. I hope readers enjoy this tribute and trip through yesteryear.

Conclusion

Upon completion of reading this book it will be difficult not to wonder how Pepoon would feel about the environmental issues of today. His writings, as technical and eloquent as they are, were written at a time when the environment was more stable, less complex, and had fewer pressures. During Pepoon's time, land disturbances were rather one dimensional. Pepoon's main complaint about land changes focused on the greed of agrarians to maximize profit by cutting timber to make way for crops and pasturing cattle and swine in woodlands. Other ecological concerns included late summer burning by railroad crews to clear brush and the lack of land acquisition by the commonwealth. Today, such concerns are generally not significant: farmers are not clear-cutting forests to make way for row crops, former pastures are returning to timber, the railroad is not burning in late summer (or at anytime) and land acquisition is protecting millions of acres state-wide. Pepoon would have been delighted with these changes in conservation. However, new, more serious threats have developed, ones that he did not see coming. This is evident by his rosy long-term outlook for Bird's Eye Primrose.

How would Pepoon have responded to the herbicides developed following World War II, the introduction and rise of invasive species that threaten our natural areas at alarming rates, the intensive agriculture employed today, the overly efficient draining of agricultural lands, the fall of the family farm, urbanization, the massive reduction of bird diversity? What of the thousands of acres in Jo Daviess County altered to make way for resort areas and the large Contained Animal Feeding Operation scheduled to be constructed down the road from his boyhood home, threatening the very river that runs through his park (2010)? What would

Pepoon's opinions be on global warming? All of these realities not only present serious challenges to bio-diversity, but threaten what he loved so much.

Today, wild turkey, white-tailed deer, the Canadian goose—all extirpated during Pepoon's time—are surviving in healthy numbers. Thousands of acres are now protected in Jo Daviess County. Prairies are being restored and woodlands are being managed. Tens of thousands of people visit his Apple River Canyon State Park annually, as he desired. Do these developments outweigh the bad?

I can't help but wonder how Pepoon would reply.

BIOGRAPHY.

IN ORDER TO UNDERSTAND these writings it is important to know the writer. Understanding Herman Silas (H. S.) Pepoon and his family history as the American frontier was transforming into modern society can help foster a more thorough appreciation of his lifelong dedication to the flora and landscape he grew up around.

The original Pepoon family (spelled "Pepon"), were French Huguenots, or Protestants, a persecuted minority in predominantly Catholic 17th century France. In 1690, two Pepon brothers fled Corsica, an island off the coast of France, eventually settling in Connecticut in 1710. They were the first Huguenots to settle in North America. It is said that Jacques Pepoon, a second-generation New Englander, introduced sweet corn to Massachusetts; for a time, it was called "Pepoon Corn" (Whitman 1930). Joseph Pepoon, Herman's great-grandfather, fought in the Revolutionary War and settled in Painesville, Ohio, in 1803, "bringing peach stones, apple seeds, and pear scions" (Saylor 2010). In Painesville the Pepoons were farmers and outspoken abolitionists; fugitive slaves on their way to Canada found shelter in their farm buildings (Saylor 2010). Silas Pepoon, Herman's grandfather, was born in Connecticut and moved to Ohio when he was 11 years old. Herman's father, George Pepoon, was born in 1832 in Painesville. On the recommendation of a friend, George and his brother Silas Pepoon, Jr., moved west to Warren, Illinois, in 1849. They traveled by boat to Racine, Wisconsin, and then by oxen and stagecoach to Northwest Illinois. Rugged pioneers, George and Silas Pepoon were among the first to settle in the Warren area, within the thriving lead mining region of Jo Daviess County, Illinois. In 1850 they induced their parents, Silas and Mary, to join them in the new open

11

country.   Many members of the Pepoon family eventually settled around Warren, with some moving further west to Nebraska (Whitman 1930).

George Pepoon, a farmer, teacher and abolitionist, volunteered for the Union Army in the Civil War with four of his brothers, one of whom did not return.   George became a decorated captain in the Civil War, as a member of the famed 96th Infantry, serving under General John Corson Smith of Galena, Illinois (Partridge 1887).   After the war, George Pepoon became the Superintendent of Schools for Jo Daviess County and was also the Warren Township Assessor and Supervisor (Pepoon 1914).   A lead mining venture, "Pepoon Diggings," was exhausted quickly and produced very little.   In 1886 he was elected to the Illinois House of Representatives.   Pepoon School on Twin Bridges Road was named after him, built on land he presumably donated.   It has been noted that George Pepoon "loved, encouraged and inspired youth" (Whitman 1930).

George Pepoon married Mary Ann Abbey in 1857.   They had two sons, William Abby in 1858 and Herman Silas in 1860, and a daughter, Mary Abby in 1868.   Herman's brother, William, was a fruit and vegetable farmer in Nebraska and, later, Oregon.   He invented and held patents on several tools and machines (University of Illinois 1918).   His sister, Mary Abby, married James Townsend and lived her life on a farm in Rush Township, Jo Daviess County.   She is buried north of Stockton, Illinois.

Herman Silas (H. S.) Pepoon was born January 21, 1860, in a stone house built by his father, just west of Warren, Illinois.   Herman grew up in a different house, the "home farm," southwest of Warren, and attended the newly built Warren High School, graduating in 1877 (Pepoon 1914).   In high school he was a distinguished student and became president of the Literary Society.   One student wrote of him: "Of all the boys in high school, Herm Pepoon was thought to be the most faithful to the rules and studies.   We emulated him.   He was our pattern.   He had 200 pounds of good nature" (Unknown 1930).   While in school, Herm was also writing poems.   One of these, *The Deserted Village*, described the former stagecoach town of Millville, the site of present-day Apple River Canyon State Park—a place Herman would be associated with for the rest of his life.

Herman left Warren to attend the University of Illinois in Champaign, Illinois, where his brother was already studying.[1]   He graduated with a degree in Natural History in 1881, then attended Hahnemann Medical College in Chicago, becoming a medical doctor in 1883.   He practiced medicine until 1892, one year in Nebraska and the remainder in Lewistown, Illinois.[2]   While in Lewistown he also served as the Fulton County fish warden, presumably to spend more time outside.   He began botanizing in Fulton County at this time, writing a paper titled *The Flora of Fulton County*.   In 1892 he left Lewistown and the medical profession.   He spent the summer of 1893 at Wood's Hole School of Natural Science in Massachusetts, completing studies "with the highest rank of anyone enrolled" (Greenwood 1955).   Herman then became the botany instructor at Lake View High School in Chicago and held that position for 38 years, retiring in 1930 when he reached the teaching age limit of 70 years.

Herman had three children with his first wife, Alma Wilcox, who died shortly after their move to Chicago in 1893.   Their children were Rudolph Silas (born July 17, 1885), Mary Lucile (August 7, 1887) and Constance Laura (December 7, 1890).   He married Helen Foberg in 1900, a former student and 1897 graduate of Lake View High School.

His daughter, Lucile, graduated from Lake View in 1906 and became a nurse.   Upon the United States' entering World War I, she told her father, "There has been an ancestral Pepoon in every war of the United States, and we must not fail now" (Osborne 1932).   Lucile did not return from the war.   She died in France on Thanksgiving

---

[1] At the time it was called Illinois Industrial University and enrolled 376 students.

[2] Pepoon's tenure as a physician in Lewistown, Illinois, coincided with Edgar Lee Masters' observances of life in Lewistown that led to the American literary classic *Spoon River Anthology*.   Masters wrote of a physician that he simply named Nature, "Until the great physician, Nature, smote me through with paralysis."

Day, 1918, and Herman accepted the Red Cross medal for her in 1921. His grandson, Rudolph Stanley Pepoon, later fought and died in World War II (War Department 1946).

Herman Pepoon was highly influential among his peers and the community in Chicago. He inspired untold numbers of students at Lake View High School in Ravenswood, where he taught botany and served as the school physician. He organized the Chicago Nature Study Club, taking students on field trips and hosting Saturday classes. Professionally, he was a member of several groups. Most notably, he served as President of the Chicago Mycological Society, and held a variety of positions with the Illinois State Academy of Science. In 1930 he was named Honorary Curator of Botany for the Chicago Academy of Sciences. Throughout his career he lectured to the public on a wide variety of subjects such as "Birds and their Habitats," "Spring Planting of Shrubs" and "Fall Fruits of Chicagoland." Pepoon's colleagues were among the most respected figures in science at the time, including Henry C. Cowles, Jens Jensen, Levi Umbach, William J. Beal, E. J. Hill,[3] and Dr. Verne Ovid (V. O.) Graham.

Joel Greenberg wrote in his book, *Of Prairie, Woods, & Water: Two Centuries of Chicago Nature Writings*, "[Pepoon] always struck me as an unusual person if for no other reason rather than he abandoned medicine to teach science at a Chicago public school. No doubt this gave him greater freedom to botanize, but he apparently truly valued his role as a teacher to be a 'molder of character'" (Greenberg 2008).

One student he "molded" was Alfred Caldwell, who became one of the country's great landscape architects in the prairie school, blending natural materials and native plants into his work. His landscape designs include Eagle Point Park in Dubuque, Iowa, and Gramercy Park in East Dubuque, Illinois (Domer 1997). Another former student of Pepoon's was Frank Caleb Gates (Greenberg 2008), who became the Director of the Missouri Botanical Garden, among other accomplishments in botany. Pepoon also had great

---

[3] Ellsworth Jerome (E. J.) Hill is the namesake of Hill's Oak (*Quercus hillii*) and Hill's Thistle (*Cirsium hillii*), among others.

influence on Wilbur Moorehead Smith, a prominent 20th century evangelistic pastor. In his memoirs, Smith writes that Pepoon nearly inspired him towards a different career, in botany:

> Dr. Herman Pepoon, whose stimulating teaching
> and great botanical studies so entered my soul
> that I soon came to the conclusion my lifework
> was to be in this field. I shall always be grateful
> for the stimulating teaching and the personal
> friendship of Dr. Pepoon, and the interest which
> he aroused in my mind. (Smith 1971)

Upon his retirement from teaching, the Lake View Alumni Association said of Pepoon, "He has made botany a beautiful and popular subject. He is without doubt, the most popular man on the teaching staff" (*The Chicago Tribune* 1941). Over the course of his tenure at Lake View Pepoon instructed over ten thousand students. According to V. O. Graham, a peer and renowned mushroom expert, each student was touched by this distinguished pedagogue:

> If we measure greatness in teaching by the
> change brought in the learner, Dr. Pepoon was
> one of the greatest teachers this country has ever
> produced. Each of his ten thousand students
> has felt his influence; his buoyant spirit changed
> work from drudgery to joyous effort.

Today, Dr. Pepoon is best known for his work outside the classroom. His books, *Studies of Plant Life: A Series of Exercises for the Study of Plants* (1900) and *Representative Plants; a Manual for the Use of Students of Botany in Secondary Schools and Colleges* (1912) are still being used as references by teachers today. *An Annotated Flora of the Chicago Region* (1927) is widely referenced by ecologists in Chicagoland and considered a classic work. It served as the predecessor to the popular *Plants of the Chicago Region* (Swink and Wilhelm), first published in 1969. Beginning during his days as a medical doctor and throughout his life Pepoon published numerous essays and newspaper and journal articles. A recurring column from 1896, "Plants to be Named," in *The American Bee Journal*, and an article titled "Gun Shot Wound to the Brain" in *The Clinique* (1893), reveal his versatility.

Following his retirement from teaching Pepoon remained active, working for The Illinois Natural History Survey, from 1931 to 1933, on the state's vascular plant collection, going on personal botanical journeys, spending time at his lake cottage near Dowagiac, Michigan and lecturing.[4]   In the fall of 1931 the Associated Press reported that Pepoon found a 60½ inch living grapevine (*Vitus vulpina*) specimen while making a personal survey of the flora of the Smoky Mountains (Associated Press 1931).   In a letter to the Smoky Mountain Park Superintendent, dated March 16, 1935, Pepoon reported 1,500 plant species found on his visit in 1931 (Stupka 1976).   In April 1941, at age 81, he discovered the largest Blue Ash (*Fraxinus quadrangulata*) tree on record in the country (*Chicago Tribune* 1941).   Numerous newspaper clippings indicate that Pepoon lectured frequently.   One such presentation, "What Illinois Offers to the Nature Lover," was made at the newly opened Stanley Theatre in Galena, Illinois, in April 1938 (*Telegraph Herald* 1938).[5]   In November 1941, a month before his death, he reportedly gave an "inspiring talk" to The Cowles Botanical Club in Chicago, sharing his plans to write more books in the future (Graham 1942).

Dr. Herman Pepoon died December 26, 1941.   Today his work is often cited in academic botanical research.   However, there are no memorials to him, no parks in his name, no awards in his honor.   The Illinois State Academy of Science, an institution to which Pepoon was loyal for 30 years, offered an *In Memory* tribute to him in their 1942 annual transactions:

> He transformed any group almost immediately
> into one of thoughtful, good natured spirit.
> In his every undertaking, constant devotion

---

[4] Pepoon named his carefree cottage *Desir du Coeur*, French for "desire of the heart."

[5] Following this presentation a tree was planted at Ulysses S. Grant's home in Galena.

and untiring energy were his priceless
contributions.   This he combined with the
ability to inspire his co-worker to great industry
by a deep and lasting interest in every detail of
each project (Graham 1943).

Apple River Canyon

One of Herman Pepoon's most notable efforts was lobbying for the
creation of Apple River Canyon State Park, down the road from his
boyhood home.   Pepoon was intimately familiar with the area and
continued exploring it throughout his life.   Oftentimes he would
bring along the Gesner brothers from Nora, who were interested
in botany, as well as his nephews, Fred and George Pepoon.   His
nephews became authorities on all pertaining to the Canyon and
did much to further the park project (Greenwood 1955).

In the Canyon on April 5, 1905, Herman accurately identified the
extremely rare Bird's Eye Primrose (*Primula mistassinica*).   This
was Pepoon's greatest discovery and was met with much skepticism
from the scientific community.   Many botanists traveled to see
this plant in person, a pilgrimage that continues today.   A 1965
article in *The Living Museum* describes the skepticism of the time.

> On a lovely April day some forty years ago, he
> discovered the existence of *Primula mistassinica*
> in the canyons.   The next year when he spoke
> before an august gathering of botanists at
> Wood's Hole, Massachusetts, he announced
> that he had collected the Canadian Primrose in
> Illinois.   His colleagues politely but firmly did
> not believe him.   Undaunted, he personally
> issued an invitation to all who would accept
> the challenge to come with him the next April
> on a primrose walk which would prove that his
> statement was true.   Many came.   They drove as
> far as they could into the canyons and then walked
> the rest of the way to where the cliffs rose above the
> river.   There Dr. Pepoon in triumph produced
> his primroses.   They exclaimed, and looked again,

and saw for themselves—*Primula mistassinica* did
indeed grow in Illinois.   (Eifert 1965).

In 1918, at Jacksonville, Illinois, Pepoon made a heartfelt pitch to
the Illinois State Academy of Science to have a state park formed
in the Apple River Canyon.   This was the first step in turning his
vision into reality.   In June 1921, 40 members of the Academy,
with members of a group called Friends of Our Native Landscape,
including the famed Jens Jensen, traveled to the Canyon for
inspection, after which they recommended it as a state park.[6]
Over the course of the 1920's The Friends of our Native Landscape
successfully lobbied and petitioned to create the modern-day state
park system.   It should be noted that Warren, Illinois, merchant
Myron Kleeberger was also important to the formation of Apple
River Canyon State Park, organizing the Canyon Club in 1919.

On July 19, 1932, the Warren State Bank received official notice that
the state had purchased the land to become Apple River Canyon
State Park.   The state passed a bill to purchase 157 acres at a cost
of $7,292.50.   On October 3, 1933, approximately 1,500 people
attended the dedication of the new park (Greenwood 1955).[7]

Legacy

H. S. Pepoon was a highly intelligent individual with an uncanny
passion for plant life, a recurring trait throughout his family
line.   Stamina, enthusiasm, and a desire to impart knowledge were
also Pepoon distinctions.   If not required to retire from teaching,
H. S. Pepoon may have never left his students.   Throughout his
life he logged thousands of walking miles botanizing, what he
called "tramping." Before his death at age 81, he was one of the
oldest living alumni of The University of Illinois.   His passion for

---

[6] According to *The News of Chicago Society,* members on this outing presented a Kenneth
Sawyer Goodman masque (musical drama) on the banks of the Apple River, reportedly
an annual tradition.   (Inspecting Apple River 1921).

[7] This dedication included numerous speakers including Congressmen Leo Allen and
Fr. Guccione, an Apple River priest, poetry was read and music was provided by the
Stockton Barber Shop Quartet.   It closed with everyone singing the *Star Spangled
Banner*.   There is no evidence to support that Pepoon was prominent among them.

the natural world kept him strong.

One can wonder how much greater influence Pepoon's writing would have if less bounded by the rules of technical research. Pepoon's style might have easily adapted to the more personal and conceptual approach of pioneer environmental writers to come. Several Pepoon scientific papers address conservation and his thoughts at times express an environmental ethic, a term later associated with the writings of Aldo Leopold and Rachel Carson. In *Flora of Chicagoland* Pepoon writes:

> The author urges upon every user of *The Flora*
> that he ever keep in mind the perishable nature
> of the wild folk he studies and that, in so far
> as he has power and influence, he exert both
> to the conservation of all our natural heritage
> that remains to us, ever needlessly maiming nor
> destroying one of our floral or arboreal citizens,
> but ever protecting them with zealous care from
> ruthless hands or ignorant caprice.

Pepoon was keenly aware of the vanishing flora before him and realistically understood the urgency of conservation. In *Flora of Chicagoland*, he describes the loss of plant life:

> The days are gone, the men are largely passed on,
> the flowers have disappeared, and into our hearts
> a feeling of sadness comes to realize that never
> again can these things be.

And the vanishing Pink Lady Slipper (*Cypripedium acaule*):

> We paused, drinking our fill and passed on, not
> one person violating the unwritten law of the
> orchid lover. An hour later, as we ate our lunch
> on the margin of the swamp, a party of robust
> young men and women from ----- college came
> along, and *each gloried* in the *rare* specimen he
> had plucked. "Cypripedium acaule, your regal
> beauty is your doom!"

Pepoon was a man of many skills and interests—a pioneer botanist, as well as doctor, teacher, author and naturalist. In May 1940, he described his deep immersion in the natural world with simple reverence:

> I am a botanist but have side lines of birds and
> beetles, beasts and butterflys, and all the wild
> folk of woodland and orchard, swamp and
> lake. All these beguile my hours. I also use
> my imagination . . . (Pepoon 1940).

H. S. Pepoon Essays

DESTRUCTION OF A FARM FLORA.
By H. S. Pepoon.

I HAVE been much interested in the movement that seems to be gathering added force as the months go by, and that has for its object the preservation of our wild plants. It certainly will receive my hearty cooperation in every possible way, the more so because I live in the midst of a people who are waging the most relentless war of extermination against a number of the most beautiful of our native orchids and lilies. It might surprise the reader to learn that I have seen 300 showy lady-slippers (*Cypripedium reginae*) gathered by a thoughtless trio in two hours' time; but so it is, and these plants are now numbered by tens when five years ago they were in troops of hundreds.

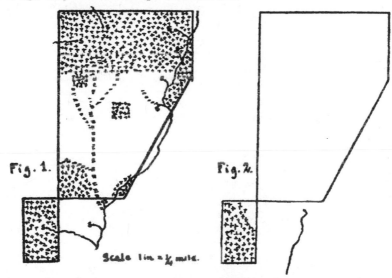

Fig. 1. A farm of 226 acres in 1876. There are 120 acres of woodland, 9 springs, and a "living" stream. The farm contains 355 species of plants.

Fig. 2. The same farm in 1904. There are only 18 acres of woodland, no springs, and no stream. The plants number only 200 species, 155 having been exterminated in 28 years.

In this same line it may be of interest to relate the history of my old home farm in northwestern Illinois. It was a woodland originally—with several "sloughs" as we called them—low-lying ravines or small valleys, very wet along the lowest level, running through from north to south. The woodlands were oak — with many "flat openings" near the heads of the ravines. The soil varied from a rich black loam in the heavy timber to a thin clay on the hillsides. Every hollow had a spring, and the main valley always possessed a fine running stream. This was at a time when 120 acres of the 226 were in forest growths.

THE PLANT WORLD

My "mouth waters" as I think of those days. The rich woods were full of red baneberry, blue cohosh, may-apples, spikenard, ginseng, shin-leaf, tway-blade, pogonia, bracted and showy orchids, yellow and showy lady-slippers, wild yams, solomon's seal, bellwort, trilliums, and jack-in-the-pulpits. Not *one* of these plants is now found on the farm. Gone they are, with the trees they loved.

To refer to what some reader may believe to be a sad blunder on my part, viz., the showy lady-slipper in rich moist woodlands: The books say in "bogs, etc."; but, alas, the books are often at fault, for in north-western Illinois these plants *always* grew in woods, or on hillsides or bluffs. Here about Chicago they behave according to the books, but not there. The beautiful calopogon had the same unconventional way—growing only on bald bluffs. In the woods with thin soil grew asters, shin-leaves, violets, lousewort, painted cups. In the "flat openings" were found wild indigo, "pennyroil," as we called it (the Koellia of to-day), pink poly-galas, purple guardias. The "sloughs" (pronounced "slew") yielded turks-caps and meadow lilies, marsh bellwort, button snake-root, closed gentian and pussy-willows galore.

All are gone. I have a list made out in 1876 enumerating 355 plants on that famed farm. To-day there are barely 200, and these are the "plebeians" and "toughs," "tramps" and "rabble" of the plant world. The royal ones are all missing.

Here the destroying factor has doubtless been the removal of the forest with its kindly influence in affording shelter and plentiful and evenly-distributed moisture. A similar fate awaits, I fear, all forest plants, for man seems determined to clear the earth of trees of natural growth, leaving it bare and desolate under the fierce heat of our summer sun.

THE CLIFF FLORA OF JO DAVIESS COUNTY.

H. S. Pepoon.

Nearly all the numerous streams that drain Jo Daviess county and, after a longer or shorter southwest course, discharge their waters into the Mississippi River, have their narrow, alluvial "bottoms" bordered by limestone cliffs of varying height and extent. These cliffs are a marked feature of the landscape, and by reason of their precipitous nature make roads having an east and west direction a very difficult proposition, and ordinary tramping across the country very difficult, and in many places absolutely impossible. In height there are all variations, from a low wall of rock, easily overlooked and overtopped by a man of average stature, to towering and vertical precipices.

Regarding the physical condition of the cliffs, there is to be found a great degree of diversity, according to the direction and amount of exposure, the amount of sunlight received, the water content of the rocks, and, to a limited extent, the diverse physical constitution of the rock itself. Some cliffs are dry as dust, others are constantly dripping cold clear lime-water; some never see the sun's rays, and others receive the full effect of the midday sun; while in exposure all gradations are found, from the sheltered nook, where a cold blast never penetrates, to a bald cliff exposed to the full fury of the north wind. All the rock is limestone and of the Galena and Niagara formations, but some variation is to be noted in the amount of sandy admixture, or in the narrow zones of chert at varying levels.

Practically all the plants found on these circumscribed and seemingly inhospitable rocks may be grouped with those of xerophytic or hydrophytic tendencies, but it is to be predicated that many of the latter are really water-xerophytes, if such a term may be used for plants that, by all sorts of protective features, try to isolate themselves from the all-surrounding moisture. Nearly all the species that exhibit a water-association habit are bog plants, of the botanical textbooks, and it is believed that they have resorted to the cliffs because of the lessened competition and the lack of the more intense struggle for existence which apparently overbalance the drawbacks attendant on the new environment.

The first noticeable feature of the flora is the remarkable mingling of the forms of the colder and warmer latitudes, although it is plainly manifest that there is a great preponderance of species of northern regions. It perhaps ought to be stated that the driftless condition of this whole area is, in all probability, the explanation in large part, for the first presence of these species from diverse latitudes. (See School Science, 1909, paper by the author.) Another marked character is the luxuriance of growth in many places, the rock soil seeming to afford very congenial habitation, and one is forced to conclude that many forms derive a large measure of their sustenance from the damp air surrounding. A third feature, and the one that adds spice to the collector's trips, is the exceeding scarcity of localities for many forms, and the further fact that they are isolated examples of species found abundantly in other parts of North America.

For convenience in studying the plants of the cliffs, it will be well to divide them into five groups acording to the physical features most predominant in their habitation:—

1. The plant-association of dripping and well-lighted cliffs, facing northerly.
2. The plant-associaion of dry and well-lighted cliffs, facing northerly.
3. The plant-association of twilight cliffs, densely shaded.
4. The plant-association of cliffs with southern exposure.
5. The transition-cliffs association.

The dripping cliffs almost invariably have an exposure toward the north and east, are usually massive, thick-bedded and towering, and very often have a most pronounced overhang, due to erosive agency of the adjacent stream. The water is always clear, cold and surcharged with lime, and often concentrated in springs. Many rock mosses form green matted layers covering the rock face, with numerous algæ intermixed, particularly Spirogyra species. *Marchantia* and *Lunulria* or, less abundantly, *Concephalus,* are liverwort forms that often clothe great spaces with a solid green covering, and winter or summer are obtainable for purposes of study or collection.

A half dozen flowering plants form an association at once interesting and attractive. The most remarkable species is *Primula Mistassinica,* which forms a thick mat-like growth, covering in one instance a space about three rods long by about six feet of vertical height, on that part of the cliff with the greatest amount of drip. The winter rosettes of this plant are well formed by September 1, and the numerous leaves evidently act as a cold protection for the innermost, immediately surrounding the root-crown, and these latter, are doubtless full of elaborated food fit for the immediate use of the plant the following spring, for in average years it is in full bloom by April 20, and then often tints the otherwise bare rock a lavender purple with the multitudes of its blossoms. By the end of May its seeds are ripe, and evidently many soon germinate, for tiny plants with but three or four root leaves are common in August. *Steironema quadriflorum* adds a brilliant hue to the green of these same zones, in July and August when nothing but the leaves of the primrose are to be seen. The yellow flowers of this species are produced in great abundance, and as a rule, the plants seem in every way more vigorous than when found growing in the ordinary boggy home of other regions. *Dasiphora fruticosus* is a very abundant form and extends vertically over much more of the cliff face, blooming until cold puts an end to its growth. This plant never assumes on the cliffs the robust habit it has in the tamarack marshes of Michigan and Wisconsin. *Galium tinctorium* is another very common plant of this association but not at all conspicuous. In the crevices and narrow ledges occasional robust specimens of *Cypripedium reginae* are to be found. So astonishingly different is such a habitat from the slough margins of Lake county,

Indiana, where this plant grows by the thousand, that one can hardly believe the testimony of his eyes, and we must needs look twice and handle to be convinced. *Parnassia* is always in evidence and flourishes. On some cliffs, notably one on Clear Creek, *Gentiana crinita* fairly covers the damp face of the rock and makes a most beautiful showing in October. This plant, however, is very local, and is not a generally present cliff species. Why it should have adopted the one locality is a hard problem. There are scattering plants of a number of other species, but the ones named are characteristic.

The dry exposed cliffs have a covering of crustaceous lichens, and a few higher forms that give a marked aspect to the plant life. *Pellaea atropurpurea* grows most luxuriantly and adds much to the beauty of the massive rocky front. *Campanula rotundifolia* abounds and shows abundantly its round root leaves, so commonly lacking in the form growing on the clay banks of Michigan and Indiana. *Solidago flexicaulis* and *memoralis* are frequent and showy in late summer. These dry cliffs, however, are the barren areas, comparatively, and large stretches are utterly devoid of plant life.

The cliffs that have such an overhang as to shut out much of the light, and in particular the gorge-like side ravines with vertical sides, almost dark at midday, have a peculiar flora, that nowhere else is found, or that appears much abated in luxuriance. These cliffs are generally damp, but rarely drip, the moisture being the general result of the lack of heat. The overhang in some places amounts to 20 to 25 feet, and it goes without saying that direct sunshine never enters. The characteristic plant is *Sullivantia Sullivantii*, which is excessively abundant, almost covering the rock in most places, and in June made daintily beautiful by its tiny but numerous white blossoms. Delayed bloom appear as late as mid-August. Here and there *Zygadenus elegans* will be found, but in the lighter parts of the cliffs. It is not, however, exclusive in its choice of a home as are the other plants named above. *Taxus* is exceedingly common on all such rocks and adds much to the beauty of the scene. On ledges an occasional *Jeffersonia diphylla* grows, but the species is a very rare one, and the seeker may climb many a cliff and never find one specimen. Several ferns are at home in these dark spots, notably *Flix bulbifera, Cryptogramma Stelleri,* and *Asplenium angustifolium.* The finding of the latter will always be an occasion of note, and the writer scoured these identical cliffs for many years before he found a plant. This simply emphasizes, however, the extreme nicety of nature's selection of habitat; for knowing the proper recipe of so much shade, rock-moisture and humus, a fine plant may now be found at any time.

The southern cliffs are not, as a rule, characteristically clothed with plant life, or rather unclothed, for they are more commonly bare. A few species, however, have here their greatest distribution. *Juniperus Virginiana* is, in places, very common, but never assumes more than the proportions of a small telephone pole, and always seems to mutely protest, by its unkempt condition, against the irony of fate that relegates it to such a place. *Aquilegia Canadensis* is often common; so is *Campanula rotundifolia,* for any bare wall dry enough suits the latter. *Pellea* is again in evidence. If the cliff happens to have a moist base, it is a congenial habitation for *Mimulus Jamesii, Epilobium adenocaulon, Chelone glabra, Caltha palustris, Salix Bebbiana, Carex hystricina,* and *Mimulus alatus.* None are characteristic.

The transition cliffs are those that connect, say, a vertical cliff facing north with a second cliff facing east, the various fronts being due to the sinuous course of the waterway that carved them out. In character they are compromise of cliff and talus, a vertical band and then a steep slope, and so on from base to summit. Having all directions of front and all kinds of soils, these places are remarkably rich in species, but very few of these latter are definitely and peculiarly cliff dwellers. These rough, untillable, non-pasturable, and largely *untreadable* slopes, have, however, a very great influence on the plant life of the region, for here are collected, for the *last* stand against the *civilized* death-warrant, a host of species that, each selecting its circumscribed dry or moist rock or sunny or shady nook, flourish as the green-bay tree. It will suffice to give a small list, to show the mixed social nature of the vegetation:— *Marchantia, Polystichum, Adiantum, Pinus strobus, Muhlenbergia* sp., *Carex albursina, Morus rubra, Caleorchis, Actaeo rubra, Caulophyllum, Bicuculla Canadensis, Arabis* sp., *Dirca, Pyrola elliptica, Chimaphila umbellata, Gentiana quinquefolia, G. flavida, Thalesia uniflora, Diervilla, Viburnum Opulus, Symphoricarpus racemosus, Betula papyrifera.* The last is everywhere, a marked and remarkable species.

This has been but a mere surface scratching of the soil, but I hope that I have made it plain that the cliffs of Jo Daviess are plant resorts of great interest and that many ecological problems are involved in the question of how such species have taken up their abode in the seemingly inhospitable soil of rock, and that, further, I have at least suggested the answer in some cases. As a conclusion, it might be noted that the seeker after plant knowledge on these precarious rocky heights may on occasion be stopping to admire the brazen beauty of the poison ivy or wonder at the innocent immaculate appearance of the deadly *Amanita* and meet (with a backbone chill) the unwinking glare of a huge timber-rattlesnake and stepping backward to avoid the triple danger, plunge downward a hundred feet into the cold river beneath.

AN ECOLOGICAL SURVEY OF THE DRIFTLESS AREA OF ILLINOIS AND WISCONSIN.

By H. S. Pepoon, M.D.,

Lake View High School, Chicago.

The Foreword.

A plan long cherished by the writer, to make a botanical survey of that portion of Illinois and Wisconsin known to the geologist as the *driftless area,* was put into active operation during the summer of 1908, when continuous exploration was undertaken for sixty days during the months of July and August. Much work of a more or less desultory nature had been accomplished before this year, extending over a period of nearly thirty years, or from boyhood days, and resulting in many valuable observations and the accumulation of a large amount of data, much of which is now not obtainable at any cost.

The Reasons for the Survey.

Two main reasons may be given for the survey. The first is that this area was the birthplace of the writer, and from boyhood on he had traversed the hills and valleys and was familiar with every mile of its territory, and the familiarity was due to the zeal for botanical collection that actuated the miles and miles of tramping, spring, summer, fall and winter. The second and important reason from the standpoint of ecology is that, owing to the unique geological history of the area, hinted at in the term "driftless area" commonly applied to it, there might be found many interesting and peculiar features of plant life indicative of problems in distribution that would have solutions found in the exceptional geological history of the region. Hinted at above, it has long been an accepted conclusion that for some reason or reasons not clearly understood, a. large part of southwestern Wisconsin, Jo Daviess County and adjacent parts of Illinois, and that portion of Iowa immediately contiguous, were not covered by the ice sheet of the glacial period, but seemed to be an island in the midst of the otherwise universal ice.

It is not necessary for our purpose to review the facts and phenomena that are adduced to prove this peculiar history, which yet are so palpably engraven on the earth's face that the merest tyro in physiographic knowledge could see erosive and not ice sheet agency as the creative factor. Reference may be

made to works by various authors, given in the subjoined foot-
note,* for a full discussion of this interesting subject.

TOPOGRAPHIC PECULIARITIES.

It is, however, pertinent to enlarge somewhat on the topography because it is so strikingly different from any other part
of Illinois to the east and south, and to corresponding regions
in the states named. The area is remarkable for the complexity and the completeness of its lines of drainage, that part
occupying the center of the survey in Jo Daviess County having
ten parallel streams debouching into the Mississippi River
within a distance of twenty-five miles and these streams and
their tributaries form a veritable network of interlocking water
courses, separated by ridges of lower or higher elevation and
varying in width from a few rods to several miles.

The result of all this complex system of depressions and elevations is an exceedingly rough land surface, oftentimes precipitous, with a total absence of incomplete drainage and pond
and lake formations, so characteristic of glaciated regions. Only
along the Mississippi River are any isolated water bodies found,
and these have their origin in the floods of the great river.

The elevation above the sea varies from 1,100 feet for the
general surface of the divides of the northeastern part, to 580
for the level of the Mississippi River at the southwest, or a
decrease in elevation along a line of twenty-five miles running
northeast and southwest of more than 500 feet. This gives for
the average slope, 20 feet to the mile; on the contrary, a line
running northwest and southeast, from the bluff at East Dubuque to Plum River Valley in the north part of Carroll County
would have elevations at close intervals, reading as follows:
Mississippi River, 600 feet; bluff at East Dubuque, 840 feet;
Menominee River, 620 feet; Ridge, 860 feet; Galena R. 605
feet; Rice Township Upland, 900 feet; Small Pox Creek, 650
feet; Elizabeth Township (N. W.), 900 feet; Apple River,
720 feet; Terrapin Ridge, 1,100 feet; Little Rush Creek, 700
feet; Pleasant Ridge, 950 feet; Big Rush Creek, 700 feet; N. W.
Pleasant Valley, 860 feet; Plum River, 700 feet; Ward's Grove,
1,000 feet. This line would be about 40 miles in length.

MOUNDS.

The northeastern part of Jo Daviess County is characterized
by a series of so-called *mounds*, very notable features of the
landscape, having an elevation of between 1,100 and 1,300 feet

*U. S. Geological Survey Vol. 3; Geology of Wisconsin Vol. 1.

AN ECOLOGICAL SURVEY

and extending with broad intervals in a northwestern and south-eastern direction from Charles Mound on the Illinois-Wisconsin line to Ward's Grove, about eighteen miles. These mounds rise at first by gentle and then by abrupt slopes from the general elevations of the surrounding regions and are capped as a rule by Niagara Limestone escarpments, which often take curious castellated forms. In size, they vary from circular forms of forty acres or less to ridges of eight or ten miles in extent, whose summits are occasionally so narrow that room is barely found for the ever present county road.

THE STREAMS AND VALLEYS.

Practically all the streams in their upper and middle courses are confined to narrow valleys with one or both borders precipitous to a greater or less degree, often assuming cliff formations, the limestone ledge varying from ten to 150 feet in height, and often with undermined bases, showing marked erosive action. A seeming paradox is found in this constant occurrence of cliff and gorge, for the county is presumably one of the oldest of emerged areas and ought to have valleys to correspond. The lower reaches of all the streams bear out this presumption, and the youthful aspect of all the upper valleys, particularly that of Apple River, is explained by the remarkable change that was wrought in ancient drainage channels by the damlike action of the glacial drift border, closing the former outlets and compelling an erosion of new and comparatively modern channels. This is strikingly shown in Apple River, whose pre-glacial source was in the southwestern part of Wisconsin, only twelve miles from the Mississippi River, and whose waters emptied into the Pecatonica River, a chief affluent of Rock River but which at present joins the Mississippi River after forcing a gorge-like passage ten miles or more long, into an ancient stream valley to the southwest. (See Leverett and others for a discussion of this theme.)

THE WOODED PORTIONS.

The whole area, except the glacial upland border, was originally in forest, but a large proportion of the land has been cleared and is now in pasture or cultivation. In a report made to the University of Illinois in March, 1908, the author estimated, after long and careful investigation, that in 1848, or about the beginning of active settlement, at least eighty per cent of the area was in forest land, while in 1908, a half century

35

later, not to exceed ten per cent was similarly covered, and much of this had been greatly depleted of its timber. This destruction of the forest growth has had a most remarkable effect upon the water supply and the amount and variety of plant life. In *Plant Life* for 1904, I have shown how on a 230 acre farm, there were in 1876, 10 springs, four living streams, 130 acres of woodland and 355 species of plants, and at the date of the paper, no springs or streams, 16 acres of woods, and 100 species of plants.

The Problem to be Investigated.

From the above resume of the topographical features, it is evident that all these peculiarities of geological history and resulting peculiarities of land surface ought to show more or less marked influence on the plant life of the various localities. It may be well to state the problems that have presented themselves, and for which solutions have been sought, passing on to detailed discussion of each. These problems stated interrogatively are:

1. What per cent of the plants of the Driftless Area are different from those of the Drift adjacent?

2. Are there peculiar or unique plants, and if so, what seems to be the source from which they came?

3. Are there characteristic northern or southern plants?

4. Is there any sudden or well marked change in the flora at the Drift border?

5. Are there any examples of isolation of species?

6. Is there any evidence of the survival of ancient forms?

7. Do the peculiarities of local topography introduce any corresponding peculiar features of habitat?

8. How does the flora compare with that of a drift area of similar latitude?

9. Has the elevation any effect?

10. What per cent of the plants are woodland or prairie, mesophytic, hydrophytic, or xerophytic?

11. What effect, if any, has the Mississippi River on the flora?

12. What families are the best represented by species?

It is not possible here to discuss at any length any of these problems or the data collected that bears on each. Some, indeed, as yet, do not admit of full answer, but it is hoped enough has been here presented to show, in part, at least, the true solu-

AN ECOLOGICAL SURVEY

.tion of a number of the more important. Nine hundred and thirty-six species of flowering plants and ferns have been located up to the present time, and of these only a few of the more striking examples can be cited under each head that will help to illustrate the deductions I have made.

DRIFT AND DRIFTLESS ADJACENT AREAS COMPARED.

The Drift area of Stephenson County, on the east, and of Carroll County on the south, compared with the Driftless region in Jo Daviess County, leads me to conclude that fully ten per cent of the species present in the latter county are not present at all, or found but rarely in the Drift counties. This condition may arise, in part, from the development of forest on the Drift-less soil, but the presence of many species point to an inherent difference, due to other influences. Full verification of this assumption is not as yet possible; more data from the outside are needed, but all the facts thus far observed tend to confirm rather than weaken the statement. Many of the examples given could be used with equal force to illustrate other parts of the paper. Some will be so used. In fact, many of the problems are interrelated in such a manner that it is difficult to treat of any one entirely by itself.

The Canoe Birch (Betula papyrifera), so common in colder America and everywhere in warmer latitudes an evident stray from some northern center, is abundant locally and has practically no intermediate stations until the shores of Lake Michigan are reached. The Rock Elm (Ulmus racemosa) is another forest tree very local. The White Pine (Pinus strobus), and the Prostrate Yew (Taxus baccata), are common along the bluffs and are characteristic. The former found again on Rock River near Oregon, and on Lake Michigan, the latter practically confined to the county. The Wild Snowball (Viburnum opulus), the Snowberry (Symphoricarpus racemosus), the Pipsissewa (Chimaphila umbellata) are shrubby plants that are at home here. Among the herbaceous forms are several ferns, Camptosorus, or Walking Fern, Cliff Brake or Pelleas, and Cryptogramma stelleri, Zygadenus elegans, the showy Lady-slipper (Cypripedium reginae), Fringed Orchis (Blephariglottis), Rattlesnake Plantain (Peramium), Bluebell (Campanula), Rock Primrose (Primula mistassinica), Rock Saxifrage (Sullivantia), and many others; common forms scarce or absent in the Drift. The only other county in Illinois where I have found any of the above is Cook on Lake Michigan, and this condition will again be referred to.

PECULIAR, OR UNIQUE SPECIES.

Speaking more in detail of a few forms, some of which are named above, it will be interesting to refer at the beginning to the Primrose. This plant is so notoriously a boreal species that my statement of its abundance on the cliffs of Jo Daviess County was received by some botanical friends with some credulity. Here on damp cliffs having a northern exposure, the plant is so common that the bare rock walls assume a lavender hue at the time of the blooming in late April. It is manifestly a migrant from the northeast, and seems here to have found its south-western limit. The leaf-rosettes are formed in August and September and persist through the winter, at least the central leaves. Square yards of rock will often be a mass of foliage in late summer. Sullivantia is another cliff plant growing on the same exposures, but it is common only on those cliffs that have a strong overhang, the plant desiring not merely absence of heat, but deep shade also. The narrow twilight side gorges are its chosen home; while not peculiar to this region, it is perhaps more abundant here than at any other station in the state. The Canoe Birch, everywhere common on the bluffs, on north exposures, as before mentioned, is found so far as the writer has observed, at no other Illinois points except near Lake Michigan, and here it forms a zone around the south end, as if it were a relic of the great ice-mass that once filled the bed of the lake, encroaching everywhere on its border. The Pipsissewa and Rattlesnake Plantain reach their highest development in Canada, far to the northeast, and here are so excessively local that only one locality has been found for each, and each contains a score or so of plants.

(To be continued.)

AN ECOLOGICAL SURVEY OF THE DRIFTLESS AREA OF ILLINOIS AND WISCONSIN.

By H. S. Pepoon, M.D.,

Lake View High School, Chicago.

(Continued from May issue.)

Species of Northern and Southern Distribution.

The area has from remote time been uncovered by the primeval waters, so that the surface has suffered merely the modifications due to erosive agencies of air and water; it might then with reason be expected that a commingling of southern and northern species would exist, and with all the more assurance because of the midway latitude of 42 degrees. During the long lapse of time some southern forms would gradually adapt themselves to a colder climate and some northern species would reverse the process. This is exactly what is found. For an astonishing example, the Pecan (Hicoria pecan) may be named. A notoriously warm temperate tree, it is yet found in the Mississippi bottom in the area, just on the 42° line, attaining a height of 90 feet, and a diameter of 3 feet, copiously fruiting also. The Coffee bean is locally common, particularly along the bluffs of the great river. The Mulberry (Morus rubra) is frequent along the Apple River, and was found in full fruit in 1908.

Not ten rods away from groups of the two latter species, Canoe Birch, Primrose, Moose-Wood (Dirca), Wild Snowball, and other cold temperature forms were common. It is true that the narrow gorge of Apple River is an exceedingly sheltered locality, both from heat and cold, and plants from either clime, by choosing the proper exposure, would easily find a genial temperature environment. Still it is no less interesting and noteworthy that they do grow in juxtaposition.

In the larger report, of which this is but a summary, a careful analysis of the geographic center of distribution of each of the 936 listed species is made, with the following approximate results, subject to modification as the completed survey of 1909 may affect it.

Plants of northern distribution and center of development, 20%.
Plants of western distribution and center of development, 3%.
Plants of southern distribution and center of development, 5%.

AN ECOLOGICAL SURVEY

Plants of eastern distribution and center of development, 18%.
Plants of central distribution and center of development, 46%.
Plants of introduced distribution and center of development, 8%.

It is worthy of remark in connection with northern plants
that the temperature of Jo Daviess county is lower than for
any other part of Illinois, often reaching a minimum of 20°-40°
below zero. This may account for the large proportion of
plants of colder regions that are found jostling with the mix-
ture from other sources.

EXAMPLES OF ISOLATED SPECIES AND PECULIAR HABITAT.

On all the mounds mentioned in a preceding paragraph, a
more or less isolated flora is found. A few examples must
suffice to illustrate this point. The Canoe Birch is common.
Nowhere else were the following species found, viz., Putty
Root (Aplectrum); Pipsissewa; Anychia canadensis; Botrich-
ium obliquium; Aquilegia; Campanula rotundifolia and Pulsa-
tilla hirsutissima also reach here their best development. Several grass species are also peculiar to the barren and
dry knobs and exposed faces of these elevations. Putty Root
has been found by me in three places, first on Benton Mound,
in this area (one plant); second on the clay lake bluff at
Highland Park, Ill., and third, in Van Buren County, Mich.,
in beech woods, no two localities having the same environment.
This is a hard problem in distribution to solve.

Cases of peculiar habitat are abundant. Three or four very
striking ones may be given, all contrary "to the books." The
showy Lady-slippers (Cypripedium reginae) of "swamps and
woods" grow here invariably on the bluffs, and some specimens
sent to the Missouri Botanical Gardens were actually clinging
to a crevice in a vertical limestone cliff. The only specimen
of Limodorum (Grass Pink) found was on the bald crown of a
high bluff, which place yielded Leptorchis loesellii or Tway-
blade; no Limodorum of "bogs and meadows" or Leptorchis
of "wet thickets and springy banks" was found. The Fringed
Gentian is a common cliff plant; this, however, must be noted,
that abundant seepage of water constantly bathes the roots of
all the above, and an explanation is given in the next paragraph.
Shrubby Potentilla, a bog plant in Michigan, is a cliff plant here.
White Pine grows nowhere but on the dry clefts of towering
cliffs. Here, too, but lower down, the Wild Snowball grows,

40

but only here, "low woods" say the books. Moose-wood (Dirca) is to be sought for on the bluffs; "woods and thickets" the books have it.

It appears to me that these peculiarities of habitat have a reasonable explanation in a gradual adaptation of the several species to life in far different topographic environment, but having a similar water content in the soil. This change in habitat may be a striking example of the effect of the removal of the fierce competition in the open bog or thicket, a few forms seemingly, discovering the practical immunity from such struggle on the cliffs and adapting themselves to life there.

This has been done even at the expense of precarious foothold and lesser food supply. Here, then, we might expect to find the last stand of many ancient as well as modern forms of plant life. The only place where the three confers, Pine, Red Cedar, and Yew, many ferns, several orchids, three liliaceous plants, the Primrose, and many more are to be found, is on these, to man often unattainable, cliff homes.

THE BORDER BETWEEN DRIFT AND DRIFTLESS.

While but little difference appears to exist in the plants of the upland varieties on the prairies, everywhere the topographic feature of the border between the two areas, one feature deserves particular mention, and that is the very sudden increase in number of pond and swamp forms, brought about by the imperfect drainage of the drift. The ponds, swamps, and wet prairies abound in sedges, juncus, potomogetons, polygonums, utricularias, naumbergias, and many more species entirely absent from the other side of that magic line, the drift margin. The prairies of drier nature are crowded with forms that reach their best development here, although many species are spread over the higher open lands within the Driftless area. The Meadow and the Turk's-Cap Lily abound, and astonishing to a degree, the White Fringed Orchis (Blephariglottis leucophoea) exists by thousands. The prairie Ranunculus, Violets, Phlox, Gentiana puberula, the cream-colored Wild Indigo, Asclepias sullivantia, Blazing Stars, and hordes of other original prairie plants greet the eye.

In this connection it is worth while noting the preservative influence of the Illinois Central R. R. on plant life. Built through this region in 1858, the right of way has never been cultivated, and the only unfavorable factor is the annual *burning*

41

AN ECOLOGICAL SURVEY

off in August. This comes too late to injure in the least spring
and early summer forms, and even many Asters and late season
types find havens of safety about telegraph posts and in the
fence rows. It is here that genuine prairie plants are to be
found, and a number of species are not to be obtained elsewhere. Of course migrant plants are much in evidence, and
probably two thirds of all introduced species can be found
bordering the track bed. The purple Cone Flower, petioled Sun-
flower, False Dandelion (Nothocalais), Prairie Gentian (G.
puberula), and Polygala incarnata are examples of species not
seen in other localities. The weeds from the railroad initial
vantage ground spread outward, and thus slowly take possession of waste places.

SAND PRAIRIE.

In the sand area of the southwest portion of Jo Daviess
county, bordering on the Mississippi River, a strip ten miles
long by one to two miles wide, there exists a very peculiar
and interesting community of plants, partaking in many of
their features of the characteristics of desert plants. The land
is a level plain, or with occasional minor elevations, having two
well-marked zones of elevation, the low and the high prairie,
a sand bluff bordering on the Mississippi, and a dune immediately inland from the bluff. A cross-section from river to
valley bluff shows six zones of plant life, each markedly differing from the others, except zones two and three.

Zone one is the alluvial bottom land covered by Sand-bar
Willow, Polygonums, Iron-weed and associated growths; zone
two is the abrupt sand bluff, having a slope of about 40° and
a maximum height of about 100 feet. Here White Ash, Sycamore, Hop-tree (Ptelea), Honey Locust, and Thorn Apples are
woody growths, and Day Flower (Commelina), Partridge Pea
(Cassia), Froelichia, Diodea, Polygonum geyeri, and several
grasses are peculiar. The dune, which is generally narrow.
and from 20 to 40 feet above the high prairie, has largely a
similar flora but the Black Oak is the abundant tree, and many
herbaceous forms are found in the shaded depressions and on
the landward slope. Among these the noteworthy one from
the distribution standpoint is Cristatella, native of the far west
and southwest.

Beyond the dune, and varying from a mere fringe to one
fourth of a mile, is the Black Oak belt of the upper prairie, or

the third zone of plant life. Here beside the oak are the gramma grasses, Anychia, Rhus Aromatica, Goats-rue (Cracca), Opuntia, and Dwarf Dandelion (Adopogon). Much of the soil is bare and excessively dry at all times. The open, elevated *prairie* was a waste originally, covered with a host of sand-loving plants, some very striking, as the Opuntias, Chrysopsis, Plantagos aristata and Purshii, Synthyris bullii, Horsemint (Monarda punctata), Puccoons (Lithospermum), Evening Primroses, Poppy Mallow (Callirhoe triangulata), Croton, Yellow Linum, Pasque Flower, and others too numerous to list. The Xerophytic characters are markedly common.

The lower prairie has a somewhat similar vegetation, but lying 40 feet or more lower, has much more abundant moisture, receiving also the overflow bluff drainage, there being no drainage lines from the ravines debouching from the great border bluffs to the river. A number of new forms, many of far western plants, are found on this lower prairie and add beauty to the far spreading level. Foxgloves, Amorphas, Bush-clovers, Poppy Mallows, Rock Roses, Oxalis, Polygalas, Blue-eyed Grasses, are characteristic forms. The Burlington R. R. traverses this level and has introduced many western and southwestern forms. One, Lotus americanus, seems, however, to act like a native, so abundant is it, but far from its recorded habitat.

The whole prairie marks a former level of the great river, when it flowed four miles wide from the ice land at the north, and this was in comparatively modern times, geologically. The surface has since been eroded by the wind, numerous blowouts with their peculiar plant forms, notably, Cristatella, Talinum, and several grasses being common present features. Three hundred and fifty species were found upon this prairie during the year of 1908, of which 20 were peculiar to the bluff and dune, 10 to the oak belt, 25 to the high, and 15 to the low prairie, the balance being generally scattered, although many species are very rare, and only a few specimens found. As a whole this prairie reminds me of the elevated plains of northwestern Nebraska and South Dakota, having many plants identical or of related species. In fact, a number of species seem to have had their original home on these western lands and by some means have found their way far to the eastward.

43

AN ECOLOGICAL SURVEY

COMPARISON.

The proportion of plants found in different plant associations or societies has not been fully worked out, but approximately the results are shown in the following tabulated form:

Drift Area—

No. of Species.	Prairie.	Woodland.	Bluff.	Sand.	Water.
850	250	445	40	15	100

Driftless Area—

No. of Species.	Prairie.	Woodland.	Bluff.	Sand.	Water.
936	25	641	140	100	30

In the table the introduced plants are scattered among the various associations.

SUMMARY AND CONCLUSION.

It is expected that 1909 will swell the above total to 1,050 species, the vast majority being pure woodland types or those found on the timbered bluffs. Only about 3% are prairie or water forms, while about one tenth are peculiar to the southwestern sand area. The north has contributed the largest number of species, outside of those of universal range. All the data seems to bear out the assumption that the land is old and that forms have been intermingled from all directions, and finding favorable environment have established themselves permanently. Further, provided there be suitable water amount for the root system, habitat, according to the books, means little and is often contradicted, species being found in the most unlooked for situations. Bluff and cliff flora are apparently asylums of many species that have found safe refuge from destructive agents that have driven them out of their original haunts. Isolated sand areas, like *Sand prairie,* afford splendid opportunity to study the effect of environment on plant features and structures, pure desert characteristics being found in neighborhoods normally plentifully supplied with water. And, more than all, the completeness and complexity of land drainage affects most profoundly the forms and distribution of plant life.

Many matters remain untouched or but inadequately treated, all of which will receive their full merits in the Report that goes to the Missouri Botanical Gardens, for whose benefit the work was undertaken. It is hoped that the season of 1909 will see the completion in satisfactory manner of the whole undertaking.

H. S. Pepoon then presented the following paper:

THE FOREST ASSOCIATIONS OF NORTHWESTERN ILLINOIS.

A large area in northwestern Illinois, which, roughly speaking, occupies practically all of Jo Daviess county, except a narrow strip along the northeastern border, and a small portion of the adjacent counties of Carroll on the south and Stephenson on the east, is or rather was occupied by almost continuous forest growth. In Illinois. as a rule, the wooded lands lie adjacent to streams, but here there is no such distribution. Ridge and valley alike have this forest covering. The accompanying map will show the distribution of woods, which sustain a remarkably close relation to that peculiar physiographic feature called the "driftless area."

A very large percent of the original woodland has disappeared before the ax and "grub-hoe," and it is no exaggeration to state that in many parts not more than ten percent of the first growth remains standing, so that the aspect of large areas is that of a rolling prairie; but even now the remaining portion is amply sufficient to form a basis for the study of the forest associations, and all the more so because each passing year further decreases the number of remnants.

This paper, therefore, will partake of the historical as well as the actual in dealing with the subject, and it is largely with the idea in mind of preserving many interesting facts of distribution that it is undertaken.

The Forest Associations are so intimately and vitally connected with the character of the soil, the amount of water supply, and the greater or less perfectness of drainage, that it

45

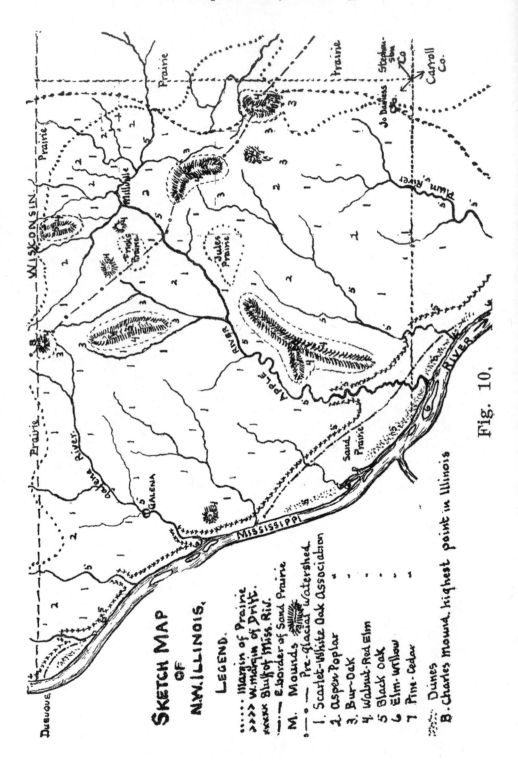

Fig. 10.

SKETCH MAP OF N.W. ILLINOIS.

LEGEND.

...... Margin of Prairie
>>>> W. margin of Drift
xxxxx Bluff of Miss. Rid.
------ E. border of Sand Prairie
M. Mounds
•∙∙ Pre-glacial Watershed
1. Scarlet-White Oak Association
2. Aspen Poplar
3. Bur-Oak
4. Walnut-Red Elm
5. Black Oak
6. Elm-willow
7. Pine-Cedar

∙∙∙∙ Dunes
B. Charles mound, highest point in Illinois

is necessary to obtain a reasonable conception of these elementary factors in distribution. No region of Illinois probably compares to Jo Daviess county in the extent and perfection of the drainage elements, for it must be remembered that we are dealing with an ancient land surface that for milleniums has been subjected to the erosive action of frost and rain, so far as we know, without a break since the days of the Niagara limestone. Countless ravines and small and large valleys cut up the surface in every directon, so that a plot of level land is a rarity, every where slopes, more or less pronounced, being the topographical feature paramount in the landscape. Only on the expanded summits of the watersheds are there any areas of poor drainage found and these are of limited extent, and yet, as shown hereafter, they are sufficiently potent to produce a forest association. The water table is in many parts very deep in the earth, this being practically true of large portions of the Galena limestone, and yet only on very limited and very local land surfaces is a genuine scarcity of water to be found. As the rainfall is about forty inches per annum, plant life rarely suffers any serious drawback from this source. The soil is everywhere the result of disintegrated rock remaining in situ except on the "bottoms" of the streams, small and large, where considerable areas of alluvium are found, and again some more or less pronounced loess soils, particularly in evidence in some of the area bordering the Mississippi river (see Soil Survey of the Dubuque Area). A clay subsoil, grayish, yellow, or even ocher red, with a few flints here and there, of many feet thickness, merges into a surface soil of clay, clay-loam, or even a black humus in limited districts, the latter particularly in evidence as border deposits where the forest and prairie join, or at the junction of Niagara and Cincinnati shales. A very limited amount of sand is found in these soils, but near the Mississippi river are several square miles of sandy soils of varying purity, evidently of river and wind formation.

Owing to the general uniformity and topography, we find

one general forest association and a number of minor ones that may be designated as follows:

a. The scarlet and white oak, a general forest growth.
b. The aspen-poplar.
c. The red elm-walnut.
d. The white elm-willow.
e. The black oak.
f. The bur oak.
g. Pine red cedar.

The scarlet and white oak association is the all pervading one and everywhere gives the general tone to the woodlands. The association consists almost entirely of the oaks named, but varies in every possible degree between a pure white oak and a pure scarlet oak growth. In general, however, there will be a small preponderance of one or the other species according as the soil has more or less humus and less or more clay. The richer the soil, the more the scarlet oak abounds, and the poorer and more clayey, the more abundant will be the white oaks; most of the trees of this association are second growth; a typical example, extending over one-half mile square, having a tree for every five or ten feet square of land surface, or 400 to 1600 to the acre. These trees will average 12 to 16 inches in diameter, 50 to 70 feet in height, and represent a time growth for the scarlet oaks of 50 years, and for the white oaks 75. Here and there large white oaks are to be seen, two to four feet in diameter and up to 300 years of age. Many such are suitable for sawmill material, but their number is very rapidly diminishing. Occasional scarlet oaks 2 feet to 30 inches in diameter are found, of a probable age of a century or more. Often there are absolutely no other tree species included, and this will certainly be the case where the soil is of moderate fertility. As the soil thins, the white oaks with an occasional shag bark hickory presents a solid front. Running to the other extreme of soil richness, there will be found a few specimens of black cherry, pig-nut hickory, red oak and very rarely a red elm and bass wood.

As this exclusive association constitutes most of the forest growth of Jo Daviess county, it follows that the two oak species are the source of practically all the wood and timber supply of the region. The height noted above nowhere approaches the till growth so commonly seen in Michigan, Indiana, and Ohio. For post timber the young white oaks are very valuable; but the scarlet oaks are almost worthless for such a purpose, having but little durability in contact with the soil.

The undergrowth in the association is as a rule more marked by its absence than presence, great portions of the woods being absolutely devoid of it. The most common shrub is the hazel (*Corylus americana*), that in some of the moister places attains a height of 16 feet and a diameter of 2½ inches. Blackberries (*Rubus nigrobaccus*) are abundant in isolated patches that bear a constant relation to abundant water, being a certain feature of ravine heads. An occasional grapevine (*Vitis vulpina*) is seen and in rich soil the Virginia creeper (*Psedera*). Of substratum trees, certain hawthorns (*Crataegus tomentosus* and *C. mollis*), the wild plum (*Prunus americana*), black haw (*Viburnum prunifolium*), and choke-cherry (*Prunus virginiana*) complete the list. The plums are remarkable for fruit variation of every size, from bullets to great oval fruits 1½ inches in diameter, green, red, yellow and variegated, acerb, sour, and sweet in flavor.

The herbaceous plants in the white oak type are very few in number, either in individuals or species, and the botanist has hard work to obtain anything of note. Only a very few plants are in any sense characteristic. *Carex pennsylvanica is* everywhere, so also are innumerable spots of *Antennaria;* in the open places *Potentilla canadensis* is common; this is certainly a scant list. As the scarlet oaks predominate, and particularly where the humus is in large amount, there is found a great increase in these forms of plant life, and individuals and species become exuberant in numbers and growth. As an example, it may not be amiss to record again what I stated in Plant World, volume VII, that on the old home farm in Warren township of this county, 230 acres in extent, and having

130 acres of the scarlet oak woodland, there were found 355 species of plants.

In the scope of this paper it will be necessary to mention but a limited number of the more characteristic forms. Nowhere is the fact more plainly emphasized than here, that the *exposure* is a dominating factor in determining distribution of plant life. In this association type it is only on northeasterly slopes that the yellow lady slipper (*Cypripedium hirsutum*) is found, and then only in dense shade. This species is very local, not more than one or two "patches" being found in a township, and it is always in close proximity to the two ferns *Osmunda Claytoniana*, and *Asplenium Filix-foemina*, both in great abundance. These patches are invariably in the moist rich shade of ravines having an eastward trend. The twayblade (*Liparis liliafolia*) is a rare associate, and *Habenaria bracteata* and *Orchis spectabilis* are yet rarer. It is worth recording here that the last species was found by me in 1891 in identically the same situation and exposure, three miles southwest of Lewiston, Fulton County, growing so abundantly as to tint the woodland with its beautiful colors. Other species not so "finicky" as to exposure are *Trillium, declinatum, Uvularia grandiflora, Allium tricoccum, Podophyllum, Geranium maculatum, Desmodium grandiflorum, Viola sororia, Sanicula canadensis, Osmorhiza, Aralia racemosa, Steiromma ciliatum, Triostium aurantiacum.*

On the flattened crests of nearly all the watershed ridges, or rather, in many cases, the broad elevations between adjacent streams are poorly drained areas, thin-soiled as a rule, and occasinally with a small circular pond, the remains of an ancient "buffalo wallow." These tracts are the ideal home of the *aspen-poplar association.* They are generally of small extent, but now and them assume the proportions of a respectable woodland. The individual trees are commonly scattered, though not infrequently forming dense growths. Here and there are small open spaces surrounded by luxuriant clumps of hazel, which send out arms and straggling bands among the aspens. Practically the only other woody plant of size is the pussy willow

'*Salix discolor*). The roots of the poplar barely penetrate the soil, which is water-saturated in spring and early summer, and often they lie on the surface for a rod or more. The aspens attain at times a height of 60 feet and a diameter of 28 inches, but more commonly they are dense growths, 30 to 40 feet tall, and 4 to 6 inches in diameter. The ultimate fate of these latter trees is the grove of scattered adults, all that remains of the former hosts in the struggle for existence.

In these aspen associations there is practically nothing herbaceous that is characteristic, except that it is here that the rare orchid *Habenaria bracteata* is most surely to be found. In the small prairies that have been referred to as certain to be found with every such association, and doubtless of Indian fire origin (see later) a few species are ever present. *Baptisia leucantha*, *Polygala viridescens* carpeting large areas, *Koellia virginiana*, *Gerardia tenuifolia*, the rare *G. auriculata*, and a few plants of *Rumex Britannica*, make up the list. As hinted, these aspen flats were prairies of considerable extent in the days of Indian control, and were continued as such by the habit of firing the grass in spring that new and fresh growth might be afforded to the game of the region. When the first white men came to the country about 1800, a horseman could ride through the open woodland or through the openings in every direction. With the coming of the whites there was a cessation of the fires, and the lodgment and growth of the wind-snow aspen seed on the moist open lands caused their gradual reduction to the small open spots which are now so characteristic.

Most of the soils on which these aspens grow are what locally are termed "hard pan," having a dense impervious clay subsoil that renders the areas very marshy in spring. Usually in clearing the woodland these places are the first to be grubbed out, on account of the ease with which the laborer can remove the tree, root and trunk. The surface roots aid greatly in this undertaking. Properly fertilized and particularly so if holes are dug through the hard pan for drainage, the land produces good crops. This hard pan explains the formation of the wallows before mentioned, which were very common on all such flat

51

lands as late as 1890, but which have now almost entirely disappeared. These circular ponds were rarely more than 18 inches deep and generally contained water during the entire year.

The remaining associations are very local, or are very much circumscribed by the encroachments of agricultural operations, but even now in the aggregate covering many square miles of Jo Daviess county. So scattered are they that they show but little influence on the general tone of the forest features, and without reference to the order given above each may be briefly considered.

While it is true that occasional bur oaks may be found widely scattered, as isolated specimens here and there, and in all probobility squirrel or pigeon sown, it is equally true that genuine associations of this species occur as fringes or limited patches, always denoting good strong soil, well drained, and in many places designated by the term "bur oak openings." The origin of such a term is obscure and I make no attempt to solve it. In general, while the bur oak is the dominant species, this association is not a pure growth, but a number of different trees is almost certain to be found. The oaks are often very large, with wide-spreading branches, and have a trunk diameter of 2 to 4 feet, and height of 80 feet, and in a typical woodland will stand 50 or 60 feet apart.

Just what the cause may be for these limited areas devoted to a particular species is not positively determined, but the conjecture is made that where the underlying lime rocks have become disintegrated sufficiently and are near enough the surface for good drainage, and where finally much humus has accumulated, such places seem to be the ideals for bur oak development. In nearly all of the best examples that are known to the writer, this association occupies the highest horizon of the Galena limestone at the point where it is overlaid with crumbling shales of the Cincinnati formation. Such a region has an abundant moisture from the innumerable springs that have their origin in the sloping steeps of the latter strata, rising in disintegrated masses to meet the weather worn escarpments of the Niagara.

An external factor, strangely enough, almost entirely precludes the determination of a peculiar herbaceous flora for this association, viz: that owing to the enormous production of very nutritious acorn food, such groves are almost invariably "hog pastures," and all wild growth has either become exterminated, or so mixed with pasture weeds as to become useless for purposes of study.

Above this growth on all the lands lying adjacent to the great Niagara mounds, so common and conspicuous a feature of the landscape of northwestern Illinois, is to be found an irregular belt or zone, occupied largely by black walnut and red elm, which here and there, by reason of the erosion caused by some drainage line, assumes the form of a great amphitheater, surrounded on all sides, but the outflowing, by the steep slopes of the mound, partly Cincinnati and partly Niagara, both taluslike in appearance. In such places the species named reach magnificent proportions, are very numerous in individuals, and are commonly associated with basswood and red oak in much less numbers. The soil is very rich, full of humus, plentifully supplied with moisture, and is by all odds the most prolific in species of any area in the entire region. Here are to be found in great profusion those species that are the rarest of plants elsewhere.

Nowhere except in the immediate valley of the Mississippi river are the trees so luxuriant. The undergrowth resembles in most particulars the rich scarlet oak type of the first association and many of the herbaceous plants are the same. From this it would seem that shallow-rooted plants find the areas quite similar, but the deep-rooted trees evidently discover something in the one region not found in the other, and this something is potent enough to produce a great difference in tree growth.

In these favored ampitheaters are to be found, among others, the following herbaceous plants various rare Carices as *C. albursina, pedunculata, plantaginea, Frankii, Erythronium albidum* by thousands, *Uvularia grandiflora, Orchis spectabilis, Asarum canadense Actaea rubra, Sanguinaria, Dicentra cucul-*

laria, Caulophyllum, Podophyllum, Dentaria laciniata, Viola scabriuscula, Geranium, maculatum, Impatiens aurea, Oxalis racemosa, Phlox divaricata, Hydrophyllum virginianum, Scutellaria versicolor, Agastache, Campanula americana.

The *black oak association* is remarkable for at least two things, viz: that commonly the oak is the only notable tree species, and further that wherever dry, barren, or eminently unfavorable land surfaces are found, there it will be certain to grow. These barren soils are to be found in three well-marked and seemingly quite different topographic areas: first, on the elevated summit ridges of the Niagara mounds; second, on the equally dry and rocky brows of the Apple river and Mississippi river bluffs; third, in the dune region adjacent to the Mississippi on sand prairie in the southwestern part of Jo Daviess county. A height of 60 feet and a diameter of 2 feet will mark the largest growths. They are generally scrawny, often hollow, and only in young trees thriftly in appearance. The most thrifty specimens are found on the tops of the mounds and in spots of some comparative richness of soil. May it not be true that the oak grows in pure sand of the dune or on the dry rocky knoll because it there finds little or no competition, and not because it would not do better on a richer soil if it were to be given possession. Seemingly an isolated species it consorts poorly with other plant growths of tree proportions.

With the black oak are to be found a very few tree species, most prominent among them an occasional great-toothed poplar (*Populus grandidentata*), June berry (*Amelanchier canadensis,*) and several species of *Crataegus.* The shrubby growth is mostly hazel, Jersey tea, and white dogwood (*Coruns paniculata*). Among herbaceous species a few only are conspicuous: various species of *Desmodium* and *Lespedeza, Viola pedata, Dodecatheon, Lithospermum canesens, Isanthus, Hedeoma, hispda, Gerardia laevigata, Liatris scariosa, Kuhnia, Aster linarifolius, A. ptarmicoides.* The sand dune flora of this oak association has some interesting additions to the above, notably *Opuntia, Rhus canadensis, Synthyris, Krigia virginiana, Tephrosia virginiana* and

54

Anychia. The oaks of this sandy district are never tall, generally very scraggy, and at best do not show any luxuriance of growth. This black oak forest, if it can be so called, varies from a few rods to three-eights of a mile in width, and extends along the Mississippi river for a number of miles, covering the river dune, and speading out over the gently rolling sandy prairie, but everywhere cut off from the forest growth of the uplands by a mile or more of sandy plain. On the bluffs, as before mentioned, the species is again found. The history of how it found a lodgment in the sand prairie nearest the river is an interesting bit of plant distribution. Probably carried by squirrels from woods adjoining the northern and southern ends of the prairie to the occasional trees of other species, as ash, honey locust and cottonwood, the acorns were covered by the drifting sand and so found soil and moisture enough to germinate and attain the tree estate. Plain grasses and other plants preclude much sand movement further from the immediate source of the sand, the river sand bars, and there is no possibility of the acorns becoming covered. It is interesting to note that the oak margin is not an even front, but is sinuous with advancing or retreating angles, indicative of the combat between forest and plain for the possession of the sands.

The *pine-cedar association* is one of vertical rather than horizontal aspect, occupying as it does all the cliffs of the Apple river and its tributaries, as they cut through the Galena limestone to reach the main stream or the Mississippi river into which it debouches. Certain sections of the Galena river also possess these cliffs and have the same trees. Undoubtedly we have here the evidences of either the *last stand* of a dying race, or the choice of such an inhospitable habitat to avoid competition, both pine and cedar having many xerophytic characteristics that fit them for life on the solid rock, into the crevices of which their roots are insinuated. The white pines attain a height of 110 feet, a diameter of 4 feet. The red cedar rarely assumes a growth of more than 30 feet. The herbaceoous plants of these cliffs have been fully discussed in the Cliff Flora of Jo Daviess county (Vol. II. Transactions Ill. State Academy of

Science). Perhaps no better illustration is needed to show that anchorage is a chief end of a tree root system, and not primarily to obtain a major amount of the plant food needed in up-building trunk and branches. Here again the writer must remark on the marvelous difference in the habitat of these two trees from the swamp home of the one in Michigan and the other in Massachusetts.

The alluvium of all the streams of any size, and reaching the greatest development along the Mississippi river, is the chosen home of the last association to be discussed, the *elm-willow*. As a matter of course, the soil is exceedingly rich but often very wet, although rarely marshy, and subject to every considerable overflow of the adjacent river. White elms are everywhere the common tree on the drier portions, assuming magnificent proportions (100 feet high and with a diameter of 6 feet). On the moister lands the soft maple grows to immense size, one specimen having a diameter of 7 feet. Near the water the black and peach willows are common, and commonly are the river bank trees. White and black ash are common, the latter in genuine swamps. Here and there are clumps of giant sycamores, that are the largest trees of the entire region. Where alluvial soil disappears and sand begins, the sand-bar willow, (*Salix longifolia*), is the dominant form, growing in dense thickets, and serving as a catch-all for all the debris of the great river, which debris is the beginning of the true bottoms.

Associated with these trees are a number of herbaceous plants that are characteristic. Among them we note *Leersia virginica* and *oryzoides, Cinna, Elymus, Polygonum* of many species, *Impatiens pallida* and *biflora, Convolvulus sepium, Cuscuta* of several species, *Stachys palustris* and *aspera, Scutellaria lateriflora, Chelone, Mimulus ringens, Lobelia cardinalis, Helianthus,* and *Solidago*.

In concluding these words about the forest trees, it will be advisable to mention a few species that may be called sporadic, to use a medical term, that is a few of one species found in a circumscribed locality, and perhaps no others known in the whole district or separated by miles of intervening territory.

The coffee bean is a marked example. A clump of six trees, 50 feet in height, occurs on the gravelly border of Apple river bottom, two miles below Millville, and no others are known until the bluffs of the Mississippi are reached, 25 miles northwest. *Morus rubra,* the mulberry, has exactly the same distribution. *Carya illinoiensis,* the pecan, occurs at one place on the elevated bottom of the Mississippi river, a single specimen 90 feet in height, and 3.5 feet in diameter, in the midst of a woodland of elm and maple. *Betula alba* is occasional along the bluffs of the Apple river, and again on the summits of Benton mound, at 300 feet greater altitude (1200 feet above the level of the sea,) and 10 miles distant. Honey locust exists as few specimens on sand prairie; *Ulmus racemosa* is seen only on the west branch of Apple river. It would be a difficult task to explain the origin of these species, some seemingly from the south, and one or two from the far northeast.

Enough has been said to give a glimpse of the tree distribution of the region, and the grouping that seems to be rational and most easily accounted for. Errors of judgment there may be, but the points of distribution are facts that I have sought the best explanation for, from the data at my command.

LIST OF TREES OF NORTHWESTERN ILLINOIS.

1 *Pinus strobus,*	22 *Quercus macrocarpa,*
2 *Juniperus virginiana,*	23 *Quercus bicolor,*
3 *Salix nigra,*	24 *Quercus muhlenbergii,*
4 *Salix amygdaloides,*	25 *Quercus rubra,*
5 *Salix lucida,*	26 *Quercus palustris,*
6 *Salix longifolia,*	27 *Quercus coccinea,*
7 *Salix discolor,*	28 *Quercus velutina,*
8 *Salix rostrata,*	29 *Ulmus fulva,*
9 *Populus tremuloides,*	30 *Ulmus americana,*
10 *Populus grandidentata,*	31 *Ulmus racemosa,*
11 *Populus deltoides,*	32 *Celtis occidentalis,*
12 *Juglans cinerea,*	33 *Morus rulra,*
13 *Juglans nigra,*	34 *Hamamelis virginiana,*
14 *Carya illinoensis,*	35 *Platanus occidentalis,*
15 *Carya ovata,*	36 *Pyrus coronaria,*
16 *Carya glabra,*	37 *Pyrus ioensis,*
17 *Carya cordiformis,*	38 *Amelanchier canadensis,*
18 *Ostrya virginana,*	39 *Crataegus punctata,*
19 *Carpinus caroliniana,*	40 *Crataegus tomentosa,*
20 *Betula alba,*	41 *Crataegus mollis,*
21 *Quercus alba,*	42 *Crataegus macracantha,*

43 *Crataegus macrosperma,*
44 *Prunus serotina,*
45 *Prunus virginiana,*
46 *Prunus pennsylvanica,*
47 *Prunus nigra,*
48 *Prunus americana,*
49 *Gymnocladus canadensis,*
50 *Gleditsia triacanthos,*
51 *Zanthoxylum americanum,*
52 *Ptelea trifoliata,*
53 *Rhus typhina,*
54 *Euonymus atropurpureus,*
55 *Acer saccharum,*

56 *Acer saccharum nigrum,*
57 *Acer saccharinum,*
58 *Acer negundo,*
59 *Tilia americana,*
60 *Cornus alternifolia,*
61 *Fraxinus americana,*
62 *Fraxinus pennsylvanica,*
63 *Fraxinus pennsylvanica
   lanceolata,*
64 *Fraxinus nigra,*
65 *Viburnum opulus,*
66 *Viburnum lentago,*
67 *Viburnum prunifolium.*

PECULIAR PLANT DISTRIBUTIONS
H. S. Pepoon, M.D.

The author in the last few years has made an extensive study of the Floras of Jo Daviess, Fulton and Cook counties, Illinois, and upon the results of his observations in these counties the following notes are based. During these plant explorations 980 species were found in the first named county, 1000 in Fulton, and 1800 in Cook and adjacent parts of Lake counties, Indiana and Illinois. A "few years" may be better expressed by the term a half life time, for Jo Daviess is the home of his youth, Fulton of his young manhood and Cook of more mature years.

During this period, stretching back 40 years, some 2500 square miles have been carefully explored, 1,000 miles of tramping undertaken and countless thousands of individuals have come under observation. The topographic features have included the bed and border lands of *Glacial Lake Chicago* with its marshes, prairies, dunes and moraines, the rolling uplands of the *Upper Illinoisan* stage of the glacial period and the *Driftless area* of Jo Daviess with its gorges, cliffs, bottom lands and elevated highlands and erosion "mounds." The accompanying map shows the relative position of these regions and other data.

It may be remarked in a generalization that the Jo Daviess area has many boreal forms, the Cook county a great mingling of boreal and temperate species, and Fulton shows many that proclaim a warmer predeliction. Possibly 60 per cent of the plants are common to all the counties named. As might be expected, weeds are far more numerous in individuals and species in Cook county, for weeds are primarily plant-tramps that utilize to the limit the great trunk railways.

PAPERS ON BOTANY

Some 54 examples of peculiar distribution are here cited with reasonable explanations of the same where explanation is apparent. The author admits that some of these explanations are possibly open to criticism and invites the same with the hope expressed that it partake of a friendly helpful nature. These examples are given in the order of their natural sequence from lower to higher forms. In a great majority of the examples named the stations are unique, in that the plants were found there and there only in the three counties. This very isolation renders the cases of distribution more interesting, and at the same time more difficult of explanation. To avoid continual repetition, the letters appended refer to the proposed explanations given in the conclusion and summary.

1. *Pellaea atropurpurea,* the rock brake, is found in the deep stone "cuts" of the Illinois Central railway west of Warren, probably five miles from any natural stations which lie south and west. Also in similar cuttings southeast of Freeport, 30 miles distant and nearly 40 miles from natural outcrops. N. W. of center of Distribution (D. C? or A?)

2. *Woodsia obtusa,* in the famous rock cut of the St. Paul railway, north of Warren. One clump only. No other stations known for the species in Jo Daviess. N. W. of center (D).

3. *Botrychium obliquum,* one plant on the Niagara limestone summit of Benton Mound. No others ever found nearer than 10 miles. Only the one station ever discovered in Jo Daviess. (G).

4. *Azolla Caroliniana,* exceedingly abundant along Liverpool road in Illinois River bottoms of E. Fulton, the only station where the plant has ever been seen, in all of the author's botanical tramps. (G).

5. *Tripsacum dactyloides,* on an alluvial border below Seville, Fulton county, the only station; along the northern limit of range. (C).

6. *Acorus Calamus,* Sweet Flag, in isolated and far separated *patches* here and there in all three counties. The writer hazards the theory that this peculiar distribution, entirely absent in countless suitable places, is due in large part to Indian planting. (B).

ILLINOIS ACADEMY OF SCIENCE

7. *Wolffia Columbiana,* exceedingly abundant years ago north of Clarke, Indiana, but absent elsewhere in all three areas. (G).

8. *Commelina Virginiana,* on the dry dune sand S. E. of Clarke, Indiana, and on the sand bluff of the Mississippi river in Jo Daviess. (See Gray 7th Ed.) (G. or I.)

9. *Allium stellatum,* one station on C. B. & Q. railway, sand prairie, Jo Daviess. (A).

10. *Camassia,* abundant in Cook; in one or two stations in Jo Daviess. A plant much used by the Indians as a food plant. (B. and A.)

11. *Clintonia borealis,* in two tamarack swamps in Lake county, Indiana. A numerous colony in each. Plainly an extension from the northeast. (C).

12. *Trillium sessile,* in woods south of Naperville and on Salt Fork of Des Plaines river. A very rare or over-looked species. Never have seen the plant in its place of growth. (G).

13. *Cypripedium hirsutum,* excessively abundant, formerly in Lake county, Indiana, equally common now in Southwest Michigan. Found in two very peculiar habitats in Jo Daviess, one on a dry wooded hillside, and the other on the crown of a limestone cliff, four miles distant from the first station. (G? or I.)

14. *Orchis spectabilis,* very rare in all counties, except in one locality in Fulton where a half acre was found absolutely a colored sheet of bloom. Probably a thousand plants here. Certainly some condition was exceedingly favorable to account for the number and vigor of the plants. (G).

15. *Habenaria leucophaea.* Until five years ago, the rarest orchid in the writer's experience, and then two finds, one in Cook and one in Jo Daviess, disabused his mind about this rarity, but puzzled him the more as to why they were there. The Cook county station was on the flat, moist prairie of a vacant property, near Elston avenue, Chicago, where many score of plants grew. The Jo Daviess station was in two grassy swales on the right of way of the I. C., where the plants flourished by hundreds. Before these finds, two plants had been seen: one on a hillside near No. 13, and one on Platte Island in Platte River, Neb., near Fremont. (E).

61

PAPERS ON BOTANY

16. *Pogonia trianthophora* has been found in five stations during all my many years of collecting. Four are far separated clumps in southwest Michigan, the fifth three plants in a Jo Daviess woodland. (G).

17. *Calopogon.* Abundant southeast of Chicago. Was found as a single plant on a bluff-crown of Jo Daviess. A remarkable habitat for the one solitary example. (I).

18. *Arethusa.* Found in a single locality: southeast of Chicago. A dozen plants in a cranberry bog. (G).

19. *Epipactus pubescens.* A single colony a rod square in a dry oak wood in Jo Daviess. Vigorous, but very strange to its surroundings. This plant is frequent in southwest Michigan, and northeast. Western limit. (G).

20. *Corallorrhiza maculata.* In a dense Jo Daviess woodland; the only station the plant has been seen in outside of Michigan and Canada. Several plants. (G).

21. *Aplectrum hyemale.* Two plants. Twelve miles apart in Jo Daviess, one on a Mound Crest, the other on a slope, both in woods. A third station of two plants under a Thuja on the bluff at Highland Park, north of Chicago. Common in southwest Michigan. (G).

22. *Salix coactilis.* A few plants on the Du Page river at Warrenville, determined by Prof. Fernald. Maine is its home. (I).

23. *Populus heterophylla.* Quite a colony north of Port Chesterton, Ind., in woods. Associated with the three common species of Populus. Far to the north of its center. Badly diseased and seemingly in a dying condition. (C).

24. *Carya Illinoensis.* A tree 3 feet in diameter and 80 feet in height, on the Mississippi river bottoms near lower Jo Daviess. Copiously nut-bearing and perfectly thrifty. (B. C.)

25. *Betula alba papyrifera.* Summit of Benton Mound, 1100 feet altitude, Jo Daviess, on Niagara limestone. Many thrifty trees. From Jo Daviess north along the Mississippi river bluffs. (C).

ILLINOIS ACADEMY OF SCIENCE

26. *Fagus grandiflora.* A clump of 5 trees in the midst of an oak wood, northeast of Edgebrook. No other known trees within 30 miles. Perfectly at home. (B. C.)

27. *Quercus Prinus.* On the rocky banks of Apple river, Jo Daviess county. Several trees and far from its home center. (I).

28. *Morus rubra.* Two trees in Apple river gorge near the last. None other ever found in the county. (C). Common in Fulton.

29. *Oxybaphus floribundus, albidus, hirsutus.* Common along the Great Western railway, west of Stockton. Far from home. (A).

30. *Nelumbo lutea.* In the great Calumet, at Clark, Ind. Many plants, but not in vigorous condition. Excessively common below Peoria. This is the plant, that wherever found, is claimed by the natives "to grow in only *one* other place in the world." (B).

31. *Cristatella Jamesii.* Very abundant on the sand dune bordering sand prairie, Jo Daviess county. Not in Gray, 7th Edition. From the far west. (I-B?).

32. *Ribes triste.* A single bush in the center of a dense wet wood northwest of Chicago. Far northern and northeastern. (B-R).

33. *Prunus angustifolia Watsoni.* Two fine thickets on the L. S. & M. S. railway, southeast of Chicago. (A. B.)

34. *P. hortulana.* A single tree. Apparently native, on margin of Little Calumet Valley, near Dune Park. Very thrifty. (B-A.)

35. *Gymnocladus.* A fine clump on a gravel knoll near the Illinois river, north of Havana, in Fulton county. A few fine trees in Apple river gorge, Jo Daviess county. Two similar clumps were found in Van Buren county, Michigan. A strange and exceedingly rare distribution. A single tree found south of Red Wing, Minnesota. (B. or possibly A).

36. *Hosackia Americana.* Abundant along C. B. & Q. railway in Jo Daviess, western. (A).

63

PAPERS ON BOTANY

37. *Callirhoe triangulata.* A colony near N. Clark street, Chicago, on sand ridge. A thriving colony on Liverpool Island, Fulton County. Abundant on Sand Prairie, Jo Daviess county. (G.-B.)

38. *Viola striata,* on the almost vertical face of a wet limestone cliff of the Mississippi river below Portage, Jo Daviess. So abundant in this strange habitat as to tint the cliff face; a marvelous place for a violet. (I).

39. *Viola pedata bicolor.* On a bold, gravel bluff in the cods, along Spoon river, Fulton county, growing over a space of fifty feet by a hundred. Never seen by author elsewhere in any of his rambles. (G?-H.)

40. *Cuphea petiolata.* One plant. Illinois valley above Havana, Fulton county (G).

41. *Lythrum Salicaria.* Wabash railway. One plant. western. (A.)

42. *Oenothera speciosa.* Two plants. Along Belt railway, Chicago, western. (A.)

43. *O. serrulata.* One vigorous clump on dry prairie west of Chicago, one clump in Jo Daviess county. (B.)

44. *Vitis Labrusca.* In occasional groups through the Dunes, southeast of Chicago, freely fruiting. Eastern. (B-C?)

45. *Chimaphila umbellata.* A large clump on summit of Benton Mound, near No. 25. Abundant in Southwest Michigan and East and North. (G.)

46. *Primula Mistassinica.* Exceedingly abundant on wet cliff on Apple river, Jo Daviess county, near Junction of Branches. Far northern. (C).

47. *Ipomoea pandurata.* Common along Mississippi river, on slope between I. C. railway and water near Portage, Jo Daviess county. Found once in Fulton on Illinois river.

48. *Salvia lanceafolia.* Great Western railway, near Elizabeth, Jo Daviess county. One clump. (A.)

49. *Castilleja sessiliflora.* Great numbers on the sand moor north of Waukegan. A western species. (B.)

64

50. *Martynia Louisiana.* Several plants in alluvium, along a road in Fulton county. (B.)

51. *Diodia teres.* Sand bluff of Mississippi river. Jo Daviess county. Common. (B.)

52. *Cucurbita foetidissima.* One plant on Wabash railway, near Chicago, existing for years. Root eight inches thick. (A.)

53. *Lepachys columnaris.* Several near No. 48. (A).

54. *Grindelia squarrosa.* Along most trunk railways. A patch over one acre in Van Buren county, Mich., now about eight years established. (A.)

Reviewing these fifty-four examples and keeping in mind their centers of greatest abundance and most normal growth conditions, the author proposes the following explanations of their present isolated or peculiar distribution as to region and particular habitat.

There can be but little question but that examples 29, 33, 36, 41, 42, 48, 52, 53, and 54 are representatives of the great host of species that are being scattered far and wide by trunk or transcontinental railway lines, the traveling seeds falling from freight or stock cars while in transit. While many such remain railway plants, others finding congenial habitats gradually expand their growing areas. None of the plants named can rightfully be classed as weeds. (A.)

It has always appeared to the author that the exceedingly peculiar distribution of the Coffee-bean, Lotus, Calamus, and some other plants not concerned in our present article, might be the result of accidental or intentional aboriginal plantings. Practically all such species had an economic value to the Indian, and it is as consistent to adopt this view as it would be in coming days to explain the presence of many deciduous fruits to the agency of the white race. In the case of the Fox Grape, all Indiana stations lie near the Great Sauk Trail which is known to have been the path of Iroquois marauders, and it seems perfectly reasonable to adopt this explanation for the isolated distribution. There are thousands of suitable localities for the Lotus in Illinois, but the actual stations can almost be counted on one hand. It does not appear reasonable to explain by any survival theory when the one here stated is so tenable. (B.)

A few of the species named are plainly the outposts of distribution, although it is very probable that in preglacial days, this distribution might have been far more extensive. The Canoe Birch and Mistassinican Primrose are good examples growing as they do on rocks untouched by the great ice cap, and ending abruptly in Jo Daviess with the advent of the drift. Such species are 1, 11, 24, 23, 24, 26, 28, 44, 46. (C).

The deep rock cuts of the Illinois Central railway furnish an artificial habitat closely simulating the natural cliffs, and it is easy to understand how Pellaea and Woodsia would flourish in such surroundings when once established. The question, however, is not so easy of solution, for how did the spores reach the cut east of Freeport nearly forty miles from natural growth? (D. C or A?).

Doubtless a few examples representing all that are left of an original host of plants that through the advance of cultivation and consequent destructions of suitable places of growth, have finally diminished to their present inconsiderable proportions. Such are 10, 14, 15. (E.)

A few are plainly a relic of the ice age, having been pushed southward by the ice and on its retreat scattered remnants persisted here and there. This is particularly the case about the head of Lake Michigan, and may account for such plants as numbers 13, 16, 18. (F.)

The majority of the balance may be considered remnants or survivals of a very much more extended flora that from many varied causes have been exterminated, and these last representatives, leading an uncertain existence until they too disappear, and the species vanish from such localities forever. The very peculiar isolated cases of the rattlesnake plantain, the pipsissewa and the coral root in the Jo Daviess flora may be such. Here it is highly probable the erosive agencies of flood and ice have carried to destruction the intervening stations, so that the isolation becomes much more pronounced. It may be the Cristatella comes here, but candidly no theory seems to fit it exactly. Far from transportation lines, in a station so removed as to be unnoticed in Gray, it offers a puzzle in distribution. (A.)

A few like the last named and the salix are an uncertain problem. (H.)

Finally one or two seem to have actually adopted a new habitat as a place of safety in the struggle for existence. Notably is this so with *Viola striata,* and its remarkable home on the wet cliffs of the Mississippi river bluff. Luxuriant to a degree and absolutely safe from extermination, it shows how survival may be brought about by change of habit. (I.)

Summarizing the causes of peculiar or isolated distribution we have,

A. Resulting from railway traffic and other commercial agents.

B. Aboriginal plantings by the Indians for food or other purposes.

C. Extension out-posts of floras with growth centers far removed.

D. Production of artificial habitats resembling in essentials the natural.

E. Destruction by cultivation, of most of the suitable habitats, isolated stations remaining.

F. Results of the glacial ice extension and retreat.

G. Survivals in the struggle for existence.

H. Uncertain.

I. Acquirements of new habitats by change in habits of growth.

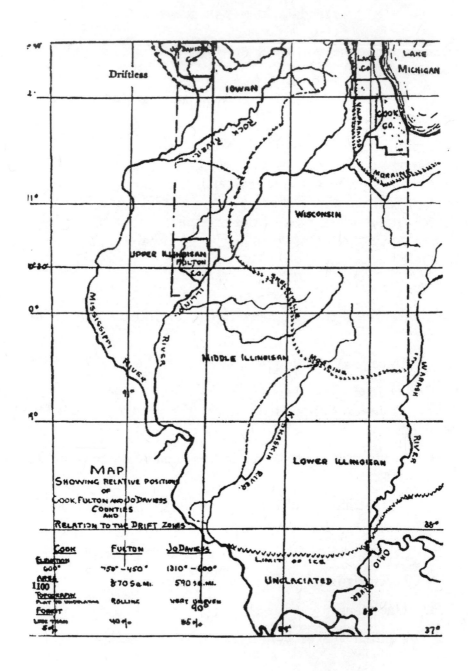

Britton and Brown, 1897

THE PRIMROSE ROCKS OF ILLINOIS

H. S. Pepoon, Lake View High School, Chicago

The 9th day of April, 1905, the writer was tramping down the narrow, cliff-confined valley of the west branch of Apple River, spying out the bird life of this sheltered locality, and more than incidentally, keeping both eyes open for the early blossoms of Hepatica, Dicentra, Claytonia, Sanguinaria and other bluff and valley species of plants. His attention was attracted to the peculiar coloration of a huge vertical cliff of limestone across and rising directly out of the river some fifteen rods from the point of observation. The whole face of the rock for perhaps twenty feet vertically and extending fifty or sixty feet horizontally was a solid hue of pale lavender purple. A "close up" inspection revealed thousands of small rosettes of delicate leaves, and springing from the center of each from one to four delicate slender scapes bearing from one to five small lavender colored blossoms. Only once before had any similar wild plants been encountered and they were the mealy primrose, growing on the rocky shores of Northern

69

Lake Huron. Evidently the new kind was a primula and a later verification made it the *Primula Mistassinica,* or dwarf Canadian primrose.

The number of plants growing on the exposed cliff was almost incredible. Some comprehension may be gained when confession is made that, remembering a good friend who was making extensive collections for herbarium purposes, four hundred and four entire plants were gathered without in any way showing that a vandal hand had even attempted to thin the ranks. So close together were the plants that practically a mat was formed by the rosettes. The leaves overlapping in all directions, as each root was on average not over two inches from a neighbor, there must have been on that favored area of rock surface not less than forty thousand plants, and these at the time above named were at the climax of their bloom, the color effect being therefore a most natural result.

A further exploration of the valley disclosed two other cliffs where a scattering growth of the plants was found, but in neither place was there any approach to the prodigality of plants, luxuriance of growth or profusion of flowers found on the first discovered area. Presumably there are other localities along this branch where the species may exist, but the fact remains, that though repeatedly visited since that year, and at all seasons, no other such find has ever been made and at this one cliff only have the plants ever been found in later years in any abundance. It is true, this lack of similar abundance and bloom may be due in large part to the great difficulty of determining from year to year the date of the maximum display. The flowers are very ephemeral and the whole cycle of the plant from beginning growth to scattered seed is barely six weeks. The varying seasons bring on the climax at different dates, the time alone when the color display is marked, and one would actually be compelled to camp on the grounds yearly for ten or more days to discover the same glory that was a purely accidental find of 1905.

Growing, as the plants do, on cliffs that are essentially vertical, there can be no question but that most of the seeds produced are lost through the agency of gravity by being precipitated into the underflowing stream. Only a mere pittance would lodge in the zone of favorable conditions. The

70

area in question is a thick-bedded and very much weathered
and eroded Platteville-Galena limestone, having many chert
seams from which year in and out there continually oozes a
lime-saturated cold clear water, giving the whole face of the
Primrose section a very wet condition. In fact the conditions
are largely the same as would prevail in a well drained swamp.
Of disintegrating rock there is abundant supply, but of humus
and ordinary soil there is practically none, and it is an interesting problem as to where the primula and other associated
species obtain the nitrogen necessary for protoplasmic needs.
The seeds that do germinate almost of necessity are caught by
some portion of the rosette or lodge on the decomposing rock
or in the numerous weathered cavities.

The constant water seepage, beside furnishing abundant
moisture and certain mineral elements, has marked ameliorat-
ing effect on the rock temperature, both summer and winter.
In summer the roots of the plant are kept constantly cool, even
in the face of the hot afternoon sun, for all these primrose
cliffs have a westerly exposure. In winter, on the contrary,
the water keeps the immediate surface and surface rock layers
above the freezing point, finally forming ice cascades that cover
most of the cliff face, and these must effectually protect from
the cold western blasts the delicate roots and crowns buried
beneath them.

This primula, as a rule, grows in a nearly pure association,
very few if any other species intermingling. Here and there,
however, there are little islands in the midst of, or peninsula
like tongues extending into the primrose growth from the margins. These are overgrown with various species of mosses,
one or two liverworts, a Parnassia, Sullivantia, Potentilla
fruticosa, Hypericum Canadense, Epilobium lineare, Steironema quadriflorum, Lycopus Americanus, Mimulus ringens,
Pedicularis lanceolata, Galium boreale, Campanula uliginosa,
Lobelia Kalmii and Senecio obovatus. It is to be especially
noted (as set forth in *Cliff Flora of Jo Daviess Co.*) that the
above list is of typical swamp or marsh species, but which all
through this particular region elect largely to grow on wet
cliffs and with even greater luxuriance than when inhabiting
the ordinary level swamp.

71

ILLINOIS ACADEMY OF SCIENCE

There is practically no danger of extermination facing this pretty species for its home has absolutely no value to man and only the wild climbing folk can by any possibility obtain precarious footing where it dwells in peace. The hog, that arch enemy of the wild plant people, can never tread these cliffs and the average human plant hog is too solicitous of his neck or extremities to venture on these slippery steeps.

In conclusion, a brief statement of the geographical distribution of our plant will be interesting. Gray, Britton, Bailey and others agree in giving it a far northern range extending well into the arctic regions of North America and reaching the United States in Northern Maine, Vermont, New York, Upper Michigan, Wisconsin, Minnesota and so North West to the Saskatchewan. This remarkable southern extension into the northwestern Illinois, therefore, is Mistassinica's "farthest south" by over one hundred miles from any neighboring station. The inference is drawn that this station is a remnant of a vast horde of the plant that in preglacial days occupied much of the rock region of Northeastern North America, the glaciers having obliterated most of these plants, the Illinois locality escaping because the ice destroyer did not there encroach.

———————

A PROPOSED NEW STATE PARK

H. S. Pepoon, Lake View High School, Chicago.

I am before you today to present and speak in favor of a Proposed New State Park, the Canyon Park, located in Jo Daviess County on the upper approaches of Apple River, a small tributary of the Mississippi. It seems hardly necessary for me to argue in favor of such a place of recreation, before a body of enlightened men and women such as constitute the Illinois Academy. All of you, doubtless, will subscribe to the proposition that within reasonable limits, all the more remarkable natural feature of a state ought, at least in part, to be preserved as playgrounds for our own and succeeding generations.

Let me, however, briefly, as stirring up your remembrance of the vital points of such a contention, that this may in turn be used by you on any doubting Thomas, state them as briefly as possible:—

The first desideratum of any commonwealth is to possess a vigorous, contented, and ever improving citizenry. In these times of fierce and uncompromising strife for commercial advancement, personal betterment, and all that goes with the modern struggle for individual and community success, the strain of labor becomes more and more imperative and exacting, and the absolute necessity for relaxation is an equally imperative call. No man, young or old, can, with impunity, and without serious danger, toil ever without play spells; for if he is able to do so physically, the reaction on the higher qualities of mind and soul are disastrous. My first contention, therefore, is that a man or woman to keep normal must play at times, must relax and give place to these higher qualities, that, in their cultivation, he or she personally, may receive enlarged benefits, and the state have developed a better and more desirable people.

73

Junction of Rivers, Head of Canyon

In the Canyon

The Primrose Cliffs

Cliff at Millville

SYMPOSIUM ON SCIENCE AND RECONSTRUCTION

My second point is, that no method is more sure of mind and soul enlargement, so that broader and higher vision may attain than to send to the hills and woods, these tired and business befogged men of affairs, and let them absorb from the ozone of air and rock, water and leaf, new and more extended outlook, with broader horizon and higher vault of heaven, with purer and sweeter breath of life, and with food and drink stimulating to more perfect growth in manly power and experience. The man who drinks in the love of Nature and studies her varied phases, is not a wrecker of the commonwealth or a despoiler of her best interests.

And again, I hold, that these schools of God's Outdoors are not merely the best places for broadening the characters and forging principles of eternal right and justice, because their influence is always uplifting and never at variance with normal development; but that further, the State has no force at its command, that, for the minimum of expenditure will produce such a maximum of increment in citizens strong in body, acute in mind, clear in vision, broad in humanity, deep in reverence, loyal in patriotism; for Nature teaches no heresy and breathes no false doctrines of social or political expediency, but ever demands the best.

When we look at the condition of affairs in our own great state, we find her woefully behind her sister and neighboring commonwealths. It may be news to many of you that our nearest neighbors on the north and west, Wisconsin and Iowa, neither possessing but a fraction of our great wealth and resources, are far more long-sighted and provident than we are. Iowa has a law on her statute books permitting and appropriating a large sum annually for the purchase of large or small tracts of land possessing desirable features that ought to be preserved and conserved for the people. In this way a lotus lake here, a fine primeval forest there, an area of cliff and stream or a piece of original prairie are bought, and a well trained corps of enthusiastic men and women are ever on the search for any obtainable lands. In this simple and perfectly feasible way, Iowa has now between 20 and 30 state parks and reservations purchased or provision made for their acquirement. It is needless to say her citizens, from Gov. Hard-ing down, are proud of this record, and well they may be, for who will be more benefited by such farsighted philanthrophy, (note the word "love of mankind") than the people themselves.

Wisconsin has already made provision for some 13 state parks, the largest being in Door County and at the mouth of the Wisconsin River, where some thousands of acres each have been reserved for perpetual playgrounds for her citizens. If one talks to those conversant with the ambitious plans of the Park people, there appears no question of the advisability and expediency of such a movement, the only problem being how to obtain as many of the desirable beauty spots before they are ruined by commercialization.

When we turn to Illinois, a very different condition confronts us. We have *one* State Park at Starved Rock, beautiful in scenery and rich in educational and historic features, and rumor is, that one or two other insignificant plats of a few acres have been acquired. But how utterly inadequate is such a condition to meet the actually needed requirements of five millions of people! We ought to have 40 state parks—large and small—to provide for this host, and Illinois is abundantly able to pay for all such lands, receiving not dollars and cents of cash in hand, but what is far more important, better equipped men and women, who will add immeasurable assets to the commonwealth.

And so I present for your consideration, The Canyon Park of Apple River, and bespeak for it your hearty support. The region proposed comprises about 1,000 acres of the wildest, roughest and most picturesque lands in Illinois, lying along Apple River from the junction of the east and west branches five miles southwesterly. This canyon is a chasm eroded in the Galena limestone to the depth of 250 feet, and it has a bottom width of 8-10 rods. The walls on either side are 45° forested slopes or vertical cliffs, these alternating from side to side as the enclosed river meanders from the west to the east rim of the canyon. The highest cliffs are 150 feet vertical walls of gray or buff dolomite unevenly bedded, full of gash veins or contraction fissure, with many small caverns, isolated towers, castles, rock masses, and huge talus blocks of all dimensions. Everywhere a forest growth rich in species, clothes

Water-worn Cliffs

SYMPOSIUM ON SCIENCE AND RECONSTRUCTION

the canyon floor, the steep slopes and all but the most exposed and precipitous cliffs. Springs, seepage areas, and side ravines and miniature canyons are everywhere, and all abounding in a rich and diversified flora. Some sixty species of forest trees and 400 species of smaller plants, many exceedingly rare, add charm to the region and make it a veritable Botanist's paradise.

As a preserve for fish and birds it is ideal. As it now is Apple river is one of the finest small-mouth bass streams of Illinois, and certain kinds of trout would certainly thrive in its cold shaded depths. The angler would find here a a place of rest and recreation second to none in the state, with a park affording protected camp sites, with neighboring farmers supplying the daily menu, and with game in the rushing waters, to tax his best skill and endeavor, there would be little to complain of. For the bird lover the varied topography and the innumerable trees and thickets make a haven that birds find specially alluring. Protected from all piercing winds of winter, with many springy places giving water at all times, with seed and fruit plants galore, many forms linger late or even winter in the canyon. For example, a jacksnipe was enjoying himself immensely Christmas day, 1918, when the upland temperature was arctic. He had a deep side gully, filled with a living spring water full of algae and small animal life, so what cared he for wintry blasts? Nearby a flock of waxwings ate juniper berries, a pair of cardinals flashed their brilliant wings, and a horde of pine siskins made the air full of their dainty twitter, whilst across the gorge a long-eared owl defied a roystering band of crows.

Historically, here was one of the happy hunting grounds of the turbulent Sauks, and in the primeval white oak forest as it stood in 1870 ancient areas of cultivation were yet to be seen. Untold wealth of arrows, spears, hatchets, and other flints attest to the esteem in which this land of vale and hill, forest and glade, was held by the red man of long ago. The ancient stage routes from Ft. Dearborn and Dixon's Ferry join not far from Millville, at the canyon's head, and thence proceeded via Frink's barn to Galena, the ancient mining town of the Indians, French, and later, Americans.

ILLINOIS ACADEMY OF SCIENCE

Ethically, scenically, historically, geologically, biologically, here is an ideal spot for *one* of the many state parks Illinois must have to keep abreast of the time and the demand, and it is sincerely to be hoped that her legislators will arise to the occasion and acquire the same, as it can now be done for a not unreasonable outlay; so that generations now living and the untold number of those to come may bless the foresight, wisdom, and broad statesmanship of those thru whose efforts fruition was at length attained.

To give a little idea of the beauty and character of the topography, a few illustrations are appended. It is earnestly urged that all who can visit this region, and learn at first hand what it has to offer of beauty and wildness, recreation and rehabiliment for all the care-worn, business fagged, mentally benumbed citizens of our great commonwealth, who here may come to renew themselves with might in the inner and outer man.

THE FOREST LANDS OF JO DAVIESS COUNTY

H. S. PEPOON, LAKE VIEW HIGH SCHOOL, CHICAGO, ILL.

PRELIMINARY STATEMENT.

Jo Daviess county, and the adjacent parts of Stephenson county on the east and Carroll county on the south, occupying the northwest corner of Illinois, are of great interest from several viewpoints, geological, topographical, and historical. These aspects are secondary, however, in the present paper to forest conditions, and it is with this latter feature that we are concerned.

The vital importance of the woodlands in the natural economy of any region is supposedly too well known to be more than mentioned, and yet it is plain, judging by actual practices prevailing among many of our landholders, that this importance is ignored. There yet seems to be much ignorance of the part forested areas play in the amelioration of local climate, the conservation of ground-water, the vitalization of stream flow, prevention of erosion of the land, the control of floods, as harbors for bird-life, or, from the aesthetic standpoint, as adding color and beauty to the surroundings, and as a valuable resource for timber, fuel, and posts. In other, less manifest, ways their addition to the sum total of rural assets is altogether too important to be ignored in their management.

THE REGION IN GENERAL.

Jo Daviess county and the areas adjoining it on the east and south may be briefly characterized as a very old region, geologically speaking, that has been rejuvenated by the influence of the glacial age so as to assume in many portions the aspect of extreme youth. Never covered by the continental ice-cap, it was nevertheless so surrounded by this great frozen flood that its preglacial drainage lines were so modified that new ones had to be substituted, and it is these new channels of erosion that make so pronounced an impression on the beholder.

81

The opinion largely prevails that the preglacial surface was a peneplain with old or mature valleys carrying off the surplus waters so that the damming influence of the glacial ice on the eastern margin changed the direction of flow of Apple River while at the same time the mighty waters resulting from the melting ice on all sides, but particularly to the north, combined to change very strikingly the ancient aspect of the surface. We find now a multitude of valleys, often with precipitous slopes, and all trending southwesterly towards the Mississippi River, with the exception of the upper course of Apple River, which follows the preglacial axis northwest to southeast. The general outcome of all this battling of the erosive powers of the past is a topography exceedingly broken up into valleys, ravines, hills, ridges, and mounds, rendering a large amount of the surface too rough for cultivation. Fully twenty per cent of the entire county is thus too steep for safe agriculture; or to express it in sq. miles and acreage, 100 sq. miles or 64,000 acres are practically untillable. All of these valleys before mentioned originally had living water courses, and while many of the larger ones yet possess streams of very erratic flow, most of the smaller drainage lines carry water only in spring or at times of especially heavy rains in winter and summer. This result, as will be shown more fully later, has been brought about by forest destruction; for it is the consensus of opinion among foresters that while forests do not in any way increase the amount or volume of water in streams, they play an important part in the fluctuation of those streams.[1]

THE SOILS.

There is no question that the ancient soil of this region was in the main the disintegrated rock of the three formations that underlie the surface, viz., the Niagara, Maquoketa shales, and Galena, more or less modified by plant growth (if any such existed in those remote ages), by wind action, and, along the valley drainage channels, by erosion. Such disintegration would have produced clays of various character, and remains of these ancient soils are in frequent evidence in many places where extensive weathering

---

[1] Diminishd Flow of Rock River in Wisconsin and Illinois and its Relation to surrounding Forests, by G. F. Schwarz. Bull. 44, U. S. Forest Service, Washington, D. C., 1913.

has denuded the surface of the more recent soil additions. These clays are, as a rule, exceedingly tenacious when saturated with moisture, and almost rock-like when dry.

Fortunately for the agriculturist, this class of soils represents a very small per cent of the whole area, and, as intimated above, it is only on the more broken and steeper land surfaces that the peculiar characteristics of the clays are clearly pronounced. Here, almost without exception, the land is devoted to woodland or pasture or a combination of both, and so soil defects play very little part in the calculations of the farmer.

LOESS.

The very large majority of Jo Daviess county soils are to be classed under the very much debated name of loess, which, in the language of the soil experts, signifies silts or silt loams. Briefly, some intelligent idea of how these soils originated may be obtained from the following visualization of a condition of the time during or following the glacial ice-cap stage in the Mississippi valley; a tremendous melting ice-sheet to the northward, sending down by the great glacial flood river, the Mississippi, immense quantities of debris of every sort resulting from the ice action; this flood of very variable volume, according to the intermittent character of the melting, now extending from bluff to bluff of the ancient drainage trough, and now very largely reduced, with immense flats uncovered and without vegetable cover, subjected to the desiccation of sun and wind.

Large impounded bodies of water covered much of the peneplain and of the drainage valleys, due possibly to overflows from the glacial margin into and over the driftless area. Prevailing westerly winds, presumably from altered climatic conditions more continuous and intense than any now existing, catching up great clouds of this desiccated and minutely comminuted soil of the exposed flats gradually losing their earth burden the farther they travelled away from the source of the soil, deposited a horizontal soil cone, or, rather, wedge, thick near the river margin and thinning to zero at an undetermined distance eastward. This mantle, covering hill, valley, mound, ridge, and every retaining surface and depositing in the great impounded waters a similar load to be modified by water action, is the "loess" of today.

The thickness of this loess layer varies remarkably, due in large part to the factor of later erosive extent, but is at its maximum depth along the western margin of the county, where a depth of thirty to forty feet has been recorded. At Warren, near the eastern border of the county, a depth of ten to fifteen feet is by no means a rare occurrence.

Among the physical characters of this loess or silt, there are several features that stand out very prominently, namely, the extreme degree of comminution as evidenced by the fineness of the soil particles, the lack of any pronounced "grit", the yellowish tint, the ability to withstand long periods of weathering and yet continue to assume almost vertical forms, the clay-like unctuousness and tenacity when wet and the angular and multitudinous lines of fracture when dried,—all these characters are more or less evident in all samples. Porosity is also marked in most varieties, giving, therefore, excellent soil drainage and at the same time retaining moisture, making this, in general, a superior crop soil.

Chemically it contains, as one would expect from its origin, practically all of the elements found in the lower stratified and igneous rocks. Largely composed of silicate of alumina, it contains also appreciable amounts of iron, lime, magnesia, potash, soda, and traces of many other minerals. It very commonly effervesces with acid, indicating an abundance of lime carbonate, and this presence of lime is further shown by the great luxuriance upon it of red clover, which thrives so well in a calcareous soil. An item of interest in connection with its chemical composition and the consequent relation to soil fertility is the experience of those farmers living in the lead-producing area. Abandoned, filled-up mine-shafts, which are always surrounded by an area more or less loaded with the deeper soil layers, invariably become veritable oases of crop luxuriance once the deep soil has become mixed with the original surface earth, which acts in fact better than manure because the effects are more lasting.

SOIL VARIETIES.

From the standpoint of forest distribution, as well as that of agriculture, the soils that are of especial importance are few in number, by far the larger part of the area under consideration having but one or more of four types of soil. In the order of their extent and influence on tree growth these soil types, are as follows: *A*, yellow silt loam; *B*, yellow-gray silt loam; *C*, the stony silt loam; *D*, brown silt loam or prairie soil; *E*. black silt loam or alluvium; *F*, rock soil; *G*, sand; *H*, black muck. The first four comprise probably 90 per cent of the soils of Jo Daviess county. Suppose that we take up a brief description of these varieties of soil, in order.

A Yellow Silt Loam.—They ellow silt loam is the extensive soil occupying most of the elevated land and slopes down to the usually abrupt declines bordering the immediate flood-plains of the streams. This soil is the chief farmland soil, and at least 50 per cent of the forest growth is found upon it. By reason of its position it is always more or less rolling or hilly, at times even abrupt, but is everywhere free from rock, usually, however, containing many flint stones of small size.

B, Yellow-Gray Silt Loam.—In a general way the yellow-gray silt loam is found on the flat summit elevations of nearly all the ridges between the lines of drainage. These flat lands are commonly called "hardpan" and are notorious for their poor drainage. It is here that all of the ancient "buffalo wallows" are found. These are circular ponds, forty to a hundred feet in diameter and from one to three feet in depth, surrounded by a fringe of marsh, caused by the buffalo of the early day standing in dense numbers and gradually stamping out a depression that became filled with water. These ponds were subsequently used as drinking-places and as a refuge in hot weather from the forest flies. So they were perpetuated until the farmer drained them, as nuisances from his point of view.

C, Stony Loam.—The stony loam occupies the steep slopes adjacent to all the larger streams, and represents the disintegrated and broken-up rock exposures, covered to a larger or smaller degree with the debris washed down from the adjacent elevated lands. The soil is usually dark and very fertile, but so full of stones of all sizes as to be totally unfit for cultivation. It is also invariably covered with timber more or less culled of better trees and, if used at all as a farm asset, is devoted to pasturage.

D, Brown Silt Loam.—The brown silt loam forms a fringe along the northeast and east margins of the region, narrowing to the west and south. It reaches a maximum width of three miles in northeastern Jo Daviess county, but extends for a number of miles into Stephenson county to the east and Wisconsin to the north. This soil is very dark by reason of its humus content and is highly fertile and almost coextensive with the drift, extending, however, on an average about two miles beyond the western margin of the same. The portion adjacent to the drift appears to have been always prairie while that portion adjacent to the yellow silt loam has been invaded by forest.

E, Black Silt Loam.—(Lintonia loam of the Dubuque soil survey.) This is the fringe of alluvium along all of the more important streams, varying from zero to a mile or more in width. Always black in color and of high fertility, this soil was originally either occupied by a heavy growth of timber or by curious narrow strips of marsh grass, resembling small prairie areas. These grasses usually occupied the very wet portions of the alluvium, and almost invariably indicated a spring or water seepage. Agriculturally this soil is the most fertile of any, but is subject always to the menace of floods.

F, Rock Soil; G, Sand; H, Black Muck.—A brief paragraph will dispose of the soils above named. The *rock soil (F)* is represented by the outcrops of the Niagara and Galena limestone. These have a vertical separation of a hundred feet or more occupied by the shales of the Maquoketa formation which do not outcrop at any point. *Sands and sandy loams (G)* are found only in the terraces of the Mississippi River and on the adjacent bluff crown. They are particularly developed in the sand prairie, a strip from one-half to two miles wide and fifteen or more miles long occupying the southwest border of the county and presenting in almost every feature the aspect of the arid western plains. These soils are coarse or fine in texture, according to their position, and are plainly river or dune formations. The *black muck (H)* soil is very limited in extent, and appears only in the bottom-lands, here and there, as undrained areas or as "quaking bogs" of limited extent and curious physical structure. The former are usually heavily wooded; the latter, never wooded.

FORESTRY SURVEY

THE FORESTED AREA

In the days before the coming of the first farmers, the wooded area of Jo Daviess county amounted to 95 per cent of the total acreage. Practically all of the open prairie land was in the extreme northeastern portion and extended as a broad belt into Stephenson county. The demands of agriculture have continually lessened the amount of woodland until at the present time only about 15 per cent remains in timber, and even this has been depleted of all the virgin growth and thinned by successive winter chopping until the actual total amount of standing timber is not more than 5 per cent of the original stand.

As examples of the extent to which deforestation has proceeded the following illustrations may be given (see maps for further particulars): Section 26, in Warren township, in 1850, in its south half, had not to exceed 20 acres of cleared land. By 1876 there were 150 acres in farm lands, while in 1918 there remained but 5 acres of thin woodland. Section 35, due south of Warren township, was in 1850 all timber; today 25 acres remain. Section 2, continuing south, which is rough land adjacent to a considerable stream, and likewise all timbered originally, now has possibly 30 acres of forest. Even in an exceedingly broken region like Section 4, the southwest quarter of which is shown in Map 4, nearly one-half of the acreage is cleared and cultivated.

That this clearing of the timbered slopes has been extremely prejudicial to the best interests of conservation in all its relations, may be easily conceded after one sees the numerous gullies washed in the slopes, effectually barring cultivation, seriously injuring pasture, causing a silting up of former clear and picturesque creeks and rivers, and ever recurring disastrous floods. One of the latter was of such magnitude that though only five miles in length, the stream, Clear Creek, running through the east half of Section 4, destroyed a stone mill-dam of seemingly indestructible proportions and absolutely wrecked the large flouring mill. When the escaping waters had subsided, some fifteen feet of silt was found on the bed of the pond, the result of the wash of the surrounding cultivated slopes, or expressed in another form, the equivalent of one foot of eroded soil from four square miles of farm land.

87

While farmers of the present day are more intelligently conducting their hill farms, there yet remains much to be desired in the conservation of the steep slopes—formerly all forest, but in many cases now deforested on the assumption that thereby much pasture is gained. And yet these same uncovered slopes, even without cultivation, often show great gullies started from some well-trodden cowpath and now assuming very threatening proportions, so that in future years, unless controlled, they will result in wreckage of valuable farm assets.

SPECIAL EXAMPLES OF FORESTED AREAS.

No 1 MAP AREA.

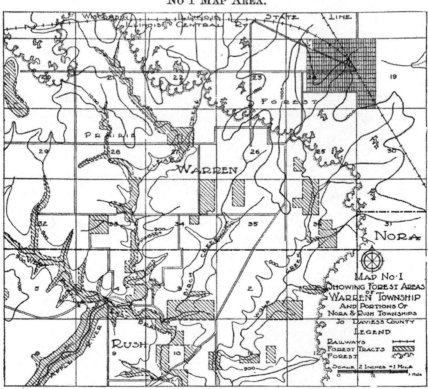

Map No. 1 Showing Forest Areas of Warren Township And Portions Of Nora & Rush Townships Jo Daviess County

LEGEND
RAILWAYS
FOREST TRACTS
FOREST
SCALE 2 INCHES = 1 MILE

By reference to Map No. 1 the extent of the present forest areas may be seen for the township of Warren and adjacent parts of Rush and Nora townships, covering an

No. 2 Map Area.

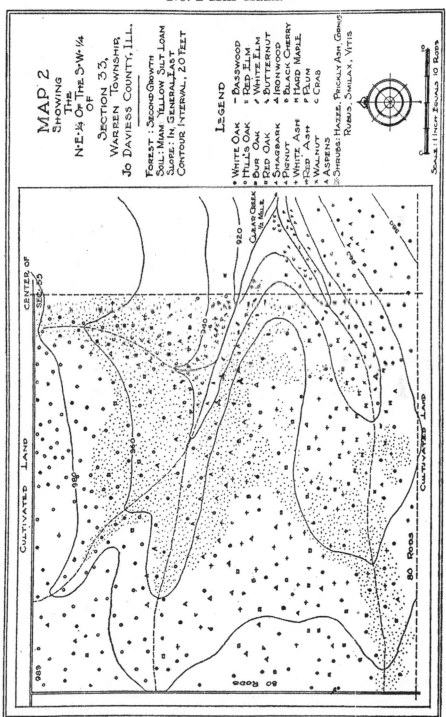

area of 32 square miles. Of this area three square miles, or 9.3 per cent, is in woodlands. The region occupied by prairie is also shown by shading. In this paper, the initial chapter of the complete report, three of the wooded areas are dealt with in detail and each is illustrated by a special map and each concerns a particular phase of the forest problem. (For details not given here consult maps 2, 3, and 4.)

One thing stands out very prominently in all of the maps shown, and that is the almost universal distribution of forest upon that portion of the surface too rough for cultivation, the wooded areas being on the streams and rough hillside slopes. There are very limited areas of really good farm land still occupied by woods. This, however, emphasizes even more strongly the evident conclusion that not a desire for conservation but unsuitability for the growing farm crops has saved these remnants of forest from extermination.

No. 2 map area illustrates what may be accomplished by permitting a stand of second-growth trees to remain practically undisturbed by the woodman or by the equally dangerous grazing stock. The soil is all yellow silt loam, the exposure being in general towards the east, but with sharper slopes to north and south by reason of a forking ravine which extends almost the entire width of the woods. These secondary slopes afford excellent illustrations of the effect of topography or slope upon the distribution of tree species. The forty acres shows well hydrarch-mesophytic associations along the lower level of the ravine, xerarch-mesophytic on middle ground, and a mesotropic association on the higher portion. While there is a marked commingling of species, in the main the type species predominates.

A very striking feature of this woodland is the very large number of young oak, ash, hard maple, and to a less extent hickory, elm, basswood, and ironwood trees. Many of these seedlings have reached the height of 6 to 8 feet and are evidently well started in a successful struggle to reach maturity. This shows better than any other fact the benefit to reproduction of keeping out cattle, sheep, and hogs. From this we may say that any forest land in this area will be able to perpetuate itself if properly protected

FORESTRY SURVEY

from grazing animals. There is also the presence of many rare or fastidious herbaceous plants that will not endure any prolonged pasturing. Among these are the coral root, tway-blades, habenarias, showy orchis, yellow lady's slipper, rattlesnake plantain, shin leaf, bloodroot, drop-seed, wild ginger, bellwort, maidenhair fern, Clayton's fern, and others equally as intolerant of "civilization" as manifested in the browsing cow and rooting swine.

A more extended and careful study of the map will show well-marked topographic zones of the particular species, which we may call forest types. The high and dry summit elevations are occupied by white oak and shagbark hickory, the former almost pure stands in some places. The white oaks are 60 feet in height and from 10 to 18 inches in diameter and represent the growth of from 40 to 70 years. The original virgin white oak forest had trees from 2½ to 5 feet in diameter, 80 or more feet in height, and from 300 to 350 years of age. The writer is informed by old settlers that in those days there was very little underbrush except in moist places, and that one could ride in any direction through the timber without difficulty. Mixed with the white oak in the proportion of one in fifty is the shagbark hickory, which is always a striking tree with its bark in great loose strips. This tree is a slow grower, averaging not more than a foot in diameter in 100 years.

A zone or belt lower down than the white-oak-hickory zone is almost entirely occupied by an oak which the natives call pin oak or black-jack oak. Up to a few years ago this was called scarlet oak *(Quercus coccinea)* by botanists, but it proves to be the *Q. ellipsoidalis* of Prof. Hill. By the former names, however, it will always be known to the country folks. The upper level of this zone contains many red oaks, white oak, red ash, and an occasional wild black cherry *(Prunus scrotina)*. The largest of the pin oak trees are about 24 inches in diameter and about 60 years old. This particular belt is always considered good soil by the farmers. The red oaks are of the same average size and age. In patches of nearly pure growth in the "pin oak" zone the two native poplars are found, each attaining a height of 70 feet and a diameter of about 16 inches. The large toothed aspen *(Populus grandidentata)* is considered much more valuable than the trembling aspen *(P. tremuloides)* for construction purposes.

91

Approaching the ravines, particularly where there are abrupt slopes, a number of trees appear in rather narrow and local communities. The ironwood *(Ostrya virginiana)* seems to prefer steep north exposures and is of rare occurrence. The hard maple *(Acer saccharum)* is found covering an area 20 rods long by 10 rods wide on a gentle south slope of the south ravine. Basswood and white elm, butternut and black walnut occur along the lower level of the ravines, particularly the south one. The last named occupies a narrow alluvial strip. It is rather remarkable that this species, everywhere considered a sure sign of rich soil, grows normally in Jo Daviess county in two quite distinct sites, namely, on alluvium and on the slopes formed by the weathered Maquoketa shale. In each case the water content of the subsoil is large in amount.

This piece of timber contains by count and ocular estimate, 12,000 trees of all species, each averaging one-fifth of a cord per tree, or about 250 cords for the "forty." This is an exceedingly conservative estimate, but even this will give a stumpage value of nearly $40 per acre. As before mentioned, such land is held in high repute for farm land and practically all of this tract could be placed under cultivation. Being owned by an outsider, it has so far escaped the fate of most of this sort of land and type of forest, and stands as a fine example of what such land will produce as forest crops. Estimating the average age of this stand as 60 years, each acre has, by the interest on the forest capital, increased in value about 60 cents a year. A special use, however, of the white oak as first-class fence-post material greatly enhances the returns from that portion where white oak grows. While as cord-wood each tree is worth about $1.50, as post timber its value is about $2.50.

The prevalence of white oak on the upper level is explained by the fact that the soil is drier and more sterile as it approaches the border of an area of yellow-gray silt loam or "hardpan" land that lies just west of this woodland. Everywhere this oak signifies thin soil, by which the soil expert means that it contains a small per cent of humus which results in scanty vegetation. And here our investigation harks back to the primeval white oak forest before pictured, with a small supply of humus and an absence of underbrush and rank herbaceous plants.

FORESTRY SURVEY

In this woodland there are four well-marked strata of growth, each contributing its quota of fallen leaves and decaying stems, as follows: A—the upper story of trees,

No. 3 MAP AREA.

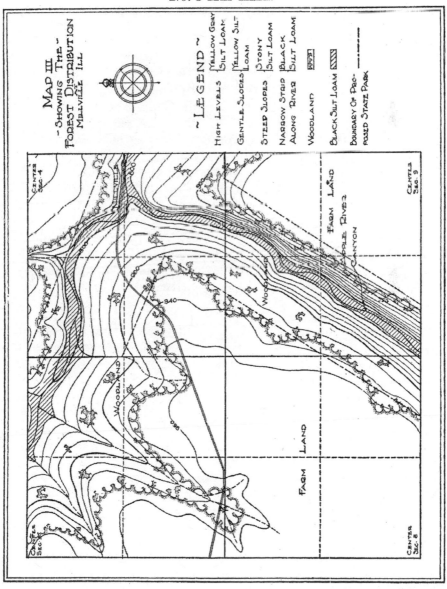

93

forming a closed canopy; B—an under story of young saplings or poles and of small trees such as chokecherry, plum, and crab-apple; C—the underbrush of hazel, brambles, dogwood, and the taller forest herbs; D—the ground-cover of sedges, grasses, herbs, and creeping vines. The better moisture conditions and the shade stimulate such growth, and this in decaying adds new richness to the soil.

The junction of the east and west branches of Apple River and the adjacent square mile of territory represents what is probably the roughest bit of topography in Jo Daviess county. Nearly one-half of the area is forest-covered, four of the characteristic soil types are well shown, and every possible difference in slope is found. Thus a rare opportunity is offered for correlating soil and forest types, as well as the relation of forest types to water content of soil and to deeper underlying strata. All of the area was originally timbered but most of the level land is now cultivated, while only the slopes, ravines, cliffs, bluffs, and a narrow alluvial strip along the streams are covered with timber. The higher levels have yellow- gray silt loam soil; the more gentle slopes have yellow silt loam; the steep slopes are composed entirely of stony silt loam or rock outcrops; while the narrow alluvial strip along the river is classed as black silt loam.

This highly diversified topography and the attendant soil variations result in a very interesting forest flora of markedly peculiar distribution; at the same time the deep canyon, freed from all bleak winds, and having a direction such as to receive the warmest rays of the winter sun favors the presence of some rare tree species and the vigorous development of many others. This canyon floor of alluvium, well watered and drained, shows very fine specimens of red, white, and cork elm, hackberry, walnut, butternut, red mulberry, rock maple, basswood, white ash, bur, red, white, chestnut and many other oaks, and, rarest of all, the coffee-bean (*Gymnocladus dioica*). Within a distance of one-half mile on a strip never more than 10 rods wide, fifty species of trees are found. (See appendix for list.) The very large walnut trees have been felled and probably two-thirds of the valley timber has been removed. The land, however, is practically worthless for any purpose except for tree growth. The cutting off of certain parts to improve the growth of pasture almost invariably results in denudation of the soil by the tremendous river floods, the standing timber, on the contrary, affording complete protection.

The steep slopes and even the rock exposures have a covering of many species of oak, ironwood, and shagbark hickory. A few white pines, red cedars, and clumps of basswood are common. The common oak is the chestnut oak *(Quercus muhlenbergii)*. A veritable jungle of undergrowth, shrubby and herbaceous, tends to make this canyon a botanical paradise, lessened somewhat in the esteem of many by the numerous rattlesnakes. These slopes, facing respectively southeast and northwest and removed but a few rods from each other, offer wonderful contrasts of xerophytic, mesotropic, and mesophytic associations. They show true xerophytic black oak, white pine, oak, hickory, xerarch-mesophytic red oak; hydrarch-mesophytic basswood, ending below in hackberry-elm, which may be called a mesotropic association. Some of the bald knobs are entirely occupied by xerophytic red cedar. These clumps are very marked and characteristic and are always practically free of other plant growth. The soil on all such knolls is from 75 to 90 per cent rock.

The upper gentle slopes and the more level higher ground is almost exclusively of the white-oak-hickory type on the drier portions and pin-oak-ash on the moister exposures, repeating here in a large measure the condition found in the area shown on Map 2. Nearly all of this forest, however, has been cleared and the land devoted to a precarious sort of agriculture—precarious on account of the steep slopes and the attendant danger from erosion. This entire square mile should have remained in forest and ought now to be reforested.

The canyon described offers a remarkable and very favorable site for a small state park, forest reserve, and fish and bird sanctuary, and it is to be hoped that the legislature of the state will see fit to take steps for a thorough investigation as to the suitability of this tract for such a purpose. Nearly 500 species of plants, including about 60 species of trees and as many shrubs, are here found occupying land practically worthless for any farm purpose except pasturage and a supply of fuel and post timber.

This map on a very large scale illustrates well the inroads made on the forest area by agriculture. Also by reference to its former forest cover, it shows the marked influence of soil on types of forest growth. Beginning

No. 4 Map Area.

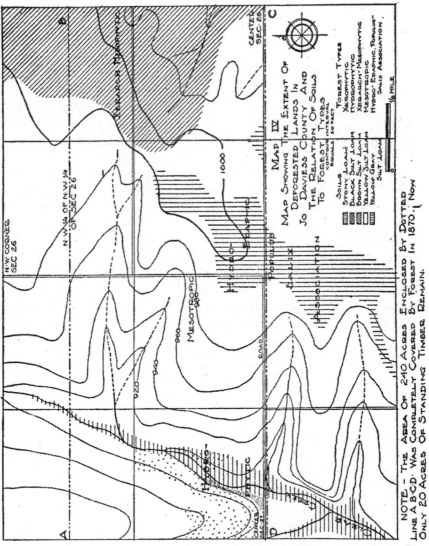

with brown silt loam on the east, there are to be found zones and belts of yellow-gray silt loam, yellow silt loam, and black silt loam, and narrow strips of stony loam. All of the 240 acres mapped was covered with forest in 1860; now only 15 acres remain.

FORESTRY SURVEY

The eastern zone of brown silt loam was originally prairie that the forest growth had usurped. Here a splendid xerarch-mesophytic forest occupied the land and in its second-growth stage represented the passage of 60 or more years. The red oak predominated, but there was a rich intermingling of black cherry, red elm, pin oak, and yellow-bud hickory. It was pre-eminently an oak growth. On the very broad yellow-silt loam zone another forest of almost pure oak prevailed, but here, on all the drier parts, white oak predominated, and in the moister situations pin or Hill's oak occurred. The ridge summit flat of yellow-gray silt loam was very largely occupied by hazel, aspen, willows, and the open, marshy grass lands having the buffalo wallows before described. None of the trees in the yellow silt hill were over 24 inches in diameter. The growth on the flat was evidently of the Populus-Salix association, and was so because of lack of drainage, the gray silt forming hardpan.

The narrow alluvium strip along Clear Creek was very largely covered with bur oak, which everywhere in Jo Daviess county characterizes the well-drained black silts, and, as before stated, the junction of the Maquoketa and Galena formations. A plentiful supply of water is one of the evident requirements of this oak. Very typical pin oaks (*Q. ellipsoidalis* Hill) were rather common also and occasional yellow-bud hickories (*Carya cordiformis*). Growing on the narrow strip of stony loam were mostly ironwood, white oak, pin oak, and shagbark hickory.

A very marked result of the deforestation of this region has been the greatly lessened surface water supply. Originally, besides Clear Creek, there were at least six minor brooks and 15 springs; today there are none. Clear Creek is only about one-fourth of its former volume and now has very high flood periods. In periods of severe drouth no soil moisture was found at times above the bedrock, which is at a depth of 20 feet below the surface, and many isolated clumps of trees had died, evidently from lack of water or lowering of the water-table. Ground-water, that formerly stood from 2 to 3 feet below the surface, is now down to a depth of 10 to 15 feet.

CONCLUSIONS.

1. Jo Daviess county was originally a forest land, and forests were encroaching on the prairies and other land at the time of settlement.

2. The original virgin timber has all been exploited.

3. About 10 to 15 per cent of the remaining forest land may be classed as heavily culled, while there is only about five per cent of merchantable timber in solid blocks. Its main use at present is for posts and fuel.

4. Most of the remaining forest occupies rough land, too steep for agriculture. By protecting this from the grazing of cattle, sheep, and hogs the forests will rapidly renew themselves.

5. A great deal of cultivated and pasture land should be reforested, since it is potentially forest land, and cutting away the forest has resulted in erosion, with all the attendant evils.

6. Practically all of the northeast slopes in the county are mesophytic or mesotropic oak associations.

7. The varieties of soil are few—over most of the area only four in number. The character of the soil not only determines the composition of species growing on it but markedly influences their growth. Forest types are closely related to soil types.

8. Jo Daviess county has some forest that should be acquired by the state as a protection forest, to conserve the water in the stream and for aesthetic and scientific purposes. Deforestation has markedly decreased the volume of water in the streams, rendering them irregular in flow and liable to floods. It has also lowered the level of ground-water from 8 to 12 feet below its former level.

FORESTRY SURVEY

APPENDIX

(Numerals refer to maps).

LIST OF TREES AND SHRUBS, JO DAVIESS COUNTY.

1. Yew *(Taxus canadensis)* III.
2. White Pine *(Pinus strobus)* III.
3. Red Cedar *(Juniperus virginiana)* III.
4. Black Willow *(Salix nigra)* II, III.
5. Peach Willow *(Salix amygdaloides)* III.
6. Shining Willow *(Salix lucida)* III.
7. White Willow *(Salix alba)* III.
8. Sand-bar Willow *(Salix longifolia)* III.
9. Pussy Willow *(Salix discolor)* II, III, IV.
10. Beak Willow *(Salix rostrata)* III.
11. Trembling Aspen *(Populus tremuloides)* II, II, IV.
12. Big Toothed Aspen *(Populus grandidentata)* II, III, IV.
13. Cottonwood *(Populus deltoides)* III.
14. Black Walnut *(Juglans nigra)* II, III.
15. Butternut *(Juglans cinerea)* II, III, IV.
16. Shagbark Hickory *(Carya ovata)* II, III.
17. Yellow-bud Hickory *(Carya cordiformis)* II, III, IV.
18. Ironwood *(Ostrya virginiana)* II, III.
19. Blue Beech *(Carpinus caroliniana)* II, III.
20. Paper Birch *(Betula papyrifera)* III.
21. White Oak *(Quercus alba)* II, III, IV.
22. Bur Oak *(Quercus macrocarpa)* II, III, IV.
23. Swamp White Oak *(Quercus bicolor)* III.
24. Chestnut Oak (Chinquapin Oak) *(Quercus muhlenbergii)* III.
25. Red Oak *(Quercus rubra)* II, III, IV.
26. Hill's Oak, (Jack Oak). *(Quercus ellipsoidalis)* II, III, IV.
27. Black Oak *(Quercus velutina)* III.
28. Red Elm—Slippery Elm *(Ulmus pubescens)* II, III, IV.
29. White Elm *(Ulmus americana)* II, III.
30. Rock Elm *(Ulmus racemosa)* III.

31. Hackberry *(Celtis occidentalis)* III.
32. Red Mulberry *(Morus rubra)* III.
33. Witch Hazel *(Hamamelis virginiana)* III.
34. Sycamore *(Platanus occidentalis)*.
35. Iowa Crab *(Pyrus icensis)* III, IV.
36. Service-berry, Juneberry *(Amelanchier canadensis)* III.
37. Cockspur Thorn *(Crataegus crus-galli)* III.
38. Dotted Haw *(Crataegus punctata)* II, III.
39. Downy Haw *(Crataegus mollis)* II, III.
40. Red Haw *(Crataegus coccinea)* III.
41. Long-spine Haw *(Crataegus macracantha)* III.
42. Black Cherry *(Prunus serotina)* II, III, IV.
43. Choke-cherry *(Prunus virginiana)* II, III, IV.
44. Wild Red Cherry *(Prunus pennsylvanica)* II, III, IV.
45. Black Plum *(Prunus nigra)* II, III, IV.
46. Wild Plum *(Prunus americana)* II, III, IV.
47. Coffee-tree *(Gymnocladus dioicus)* III.
48. Honey Locust *(Gleditsia triacanthos)* III.
49. Prickly Ash *(Xanthoxylum clava-herculis)* II, III.
50. Staghorn Sumach *(Rhus typhina)* III.
51. Sugar Maple *(Acer saccharum)* II, III.
52. Black Maple *(Acer saccharum-nigrum)* III.
53. Silver Maple *(Acer saccharinum)* III.
54. Box-elder *(Acer negundo)* II, III.
55. Basswood *(Tilia americana)* II, III.
56. White Ash *(Fraxinus americana)* II, III.
57. Red Ash *(Fraxinus pennsylvanica)* II.
58. Green Ash *(Fraxinus lanceolata)* III.
59. Black Ash *(Fraxinus nigra)* III.
60. Wild Snowball *(Viburnum opulus americanum)* III.
61. Sheepberry *(Viburnum lentago)* II, III.
62. Black Haw *(Viburnum prunifolium)* III.

PROPOSED
PARK AREAS
IN THE STATE OF
ILLINOIS

A REPORT
WITH
RECOMMENDATIONS

Published by THE FRIENDS OF OUR NATIVE LANDSCAPE
CHICAGO

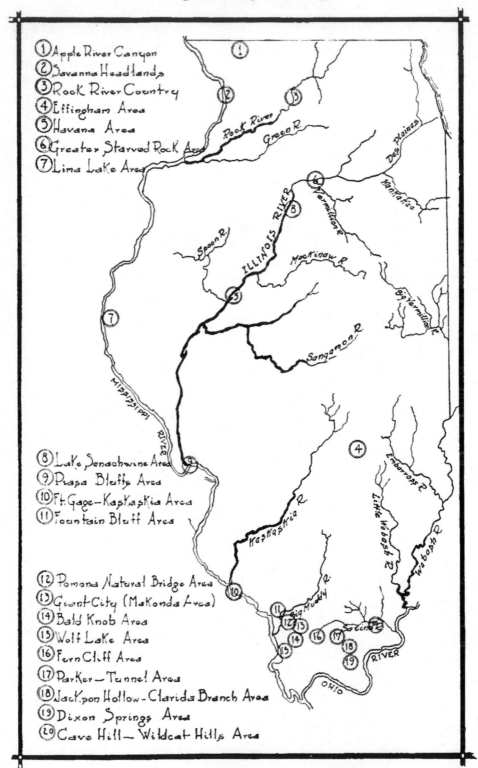

1. Apple River Canyon
2. Savanna Headlands
3. Rock River Country
4. Effingham Area
5. Havana Area
6. Greater Starved Rock Area
7. Lima Lake Area

8. Lake Senachwine Area
9. Piasa Bluffs Area
10. Ft. Gage - Kaskaskia Area
11. Fountain Bluff Area

12. Pomona Natural Bridge Area
13. Giant City (Makonda Area)
14. Bald Knob Area
15. Wolf Lake Area
16. Fern Cliff Area
17. Parker - Tunnel Area
18. Jackson Hollow - Clarida Branch Area
19. Dixon Springs Area
20. Cave Hill - Wildcat Hills Area

The Apple River Canyon of Jo Daviess County

In Apple River Canyon

In the Apple River Country

The Apple River Canyon of Jo Daviess County

HERMAN S. PEPOON

A Proposed State Park Site

An area to be set aside as a State Park for the perpetual use and pleasure of its citizens should have a number of prominent outstanding characteristics or qualities: (1) As far as possible it should be in the *original condition* with as little evidence of man's interference as is consistent with accessibility: (2) The topographic features should be striking and diversified: (3) Forest growth should be much in quantity and pleasing in quality: (4) Water, pure and natural, should be well distributed: (5) The site should be easy of access by steam and auto roads: (6) Historical values would add much to the interest: (7) Nearness to supplies so that campers may not find their pleasure marred by precarious necessities of life, is imperative, and, lastly, (8) The neighboring citizenry should be friendly to such a location so that best results may accrue.

104

Proposed Park Areas of Illinois

Measured by such standards our state has no place that can be considered more entitled to recommendation than the Canyon of Apple River. This canyon is 138 miles north by west of Chicago, lying between the Illinois Central and Great Western Railways, five miles from each; three miles from the Grant Highway, five miles from Warren, seven miles from Stockton. Its beginning is three miles

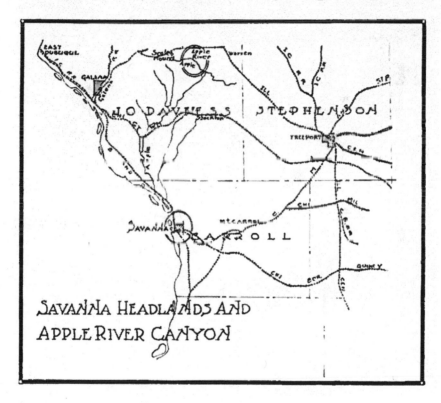

SAVANNA HEADLANDS AND
APPLE RIVER CANYON

south of the Illinois-Wisconsin line and its full extent lies within the boundary of Rush Township, Jo Daviess County.

The canyon is a water formed gorge cut into the Galena dolomite and its length of five miles wearing through that formation from summit to base, or 250 vertical feet. The rocks are more or less precipitous, often forming cliffs from 50 to 150 feet in height. Everywhere the remaining slopes vary little from 45 or more degrees. The gorge floor is rarely ever more than ten rods wide, the upper width less

The Apple River Canyon

Shelving Walls in Apple River Canyon

250 feet and for much of the distance approximates the latter figure. The direction is almost exactly N.E.-S.W., the outflow being the latter, but minor curves add to the beauty and charm. The rocks are a gray-buff dolomitic limestone in massive or thin strata, much mingled with chert seams, and on exposed bluffs often assuming striking or fantastic forms of castles, towers and the like. Fossils are numerous at certain horizons. The sheer cliffs are often tinted with the prolific lichen flora.

The Apple River which has carved the canyon rises on the state line, 15 miles northwestward, and near West Point, 8 miles eastward, the two forks uniting at Millville at the immediate entrance to the canyon. Jo Daviess County is a driftless area, the Illinoisan glacier separating northward and passing by to the east at the Jo Daviess-Stephenson County line, and westwardly a little beyond the present Mississippi. In preglacial days the state line source was the only one, the river passing the present site of Millville, flowing through the east branch course for two miles and then along the present valley of Mud Run and

Proposed Park Areas of Illinois

then Yellow Creek valley into the Pecatonica near where Freeport now is located. The glacier above referred to dammed this ancient river valley and turned the accumulated waters of Apple River southwest over what was probably a low divide, into the waters of a preglacial tributary of the Mississippi River. Thus began the cutting down of the canyon, which we see today in all its extent and beauty, not a finished product but yet in the formative period.

The river iself is a small stream of clear cool water flowing about 100 cu. ft. a second at ordinary stage. Its course is marked by long and wide stretches of quiet deep water invariably at the bases of great cliffs, alternating with crossing riffles of shoal water where the river passes from one side of its narrow valley to the other. For example—in a distance from Millville of one and one-half miles there are fifteen crossings and the same number of pools. The bed is always rock, either the solid bed rock of the deeps or the loose worn rubble of the riffles. Springs abound, adding volume and coolness and affording many places of refreshment. The side gulches, numerous and exceedingly pic-

A Flood Plain in Apple River Canyon

The Apple River Canyon

turesque, commonly bring to the main stream small additions in the form of cold sparkling rivulets.

With the exception of an occasional bald and sheer precipice of stone, vegetation is everywhere. Sixty or more varieties of trees are found within the first mile of the canyon's course. Shrubs and vines are rampant—nearly 500 species of herbaceous plants, many with beautiful bloom, grace the valley, the slopes and the rocks and crags. Rare forms abound, finding congenial habitat in the sheltered depths of the canyon where no cold and blighting north wind ever blows. Since the seas of the Ordovician Period receded an interrupted reign of sun and rain, frost and sleet has stimulated the growth and luxuriance of what must be very ancient habitants of this field Elysian.

The stream abounds with small-mouth black bass and other brethren. The wolf, the fox, the mink, the raccoon, and many weaker forest folks and swarms of birds, resident, summer visitors or migrants, invite to study or entertainment, and the crowning point will be when all these charms and treasures of water, rock, tree, flower, beast and bird are taken under the protecting care of creation's master and so conserved and preserved for the sons and daughters of men for all time to come.

THE FLORA OF THE RIGHT OF WAY OF THE ILLINOIS CENTRAL RAILWAY:

Waddams to East Dubuque.

H. S. PEPOON, M. D. LAKE VIEW HIGH SCHOOL, CHICAGO.

The author has traversed various portions of the territory covered by this paper, and during two summer vacations, walked the line from Waddams to East Dubuque, and from East Dubuque to Waddams.

It is to be taken for granted that this trip of about fifty miles was not made in one day, but, as it were, by the relay method. To illustrate the procedure, an early morning train was taken to Portage, some 16 miles from East Dubuque, and from 9 to 4 occupied in walking this portion. Another time, the Burlington train dropped three of us at Galena Junction (just across the Galena River from Portage), at 3:30 A. M., and our trip then extended until darkness overtook us in the outskirts of the western terminus; so by similar stages, back and forth, at various seasons, the ground has been thoroughly explored.

A somewhat extended statement is necessary to give a clear idea of why this stretch of railway was taken as a plant survey area. The Illinois Central was built from Freeport to East Dubuque in and near the year 1858, long before much of the land was under cultivation, and while 90 percent of the forest lands were as yet uncut. This one factor accounts for such features as small areas of "Original Prairie", something very hard to find in these days—undisturbed and unpastured *marsh lands*—bits of *original cliff* and steep *ravine sides*—*slough* remnants on the Mississippi bottoms—a portion of a western sandy plain epitomized in N. W. Illinois by a northward extension of the noted Sand Prairie of Jo Daviess—Carroll county.

Along the Galena and Mississippi Rivers are numerous places where deep and rugged ravines, and great jumbled rock masses or cliffs afford for all time, havens of refuge for many rare plants, simply because the section men, however laudable their desire may be to keep neat and clean the right of way, cannot mow or burn such spots. This

PAPERS ON BIOLOGY AND AGRICULTURE

burning business is a dire catastrophe for many plants. The writer tried to induce the Illinois Central in the days of Mr. Wallace, to permit certain *placarded* areas to go unmowed and unburnt. The Railroad's answer was "No", because of fire hazard to surrounding farm crops. Certain of the marshes and ponds, and slough margins are too wet either to mow or burn. Here then, are the last stands of many notable plants. Long may it be before the ponds dry up.

Waddams at our eastern limit, is on the highest peak of the right of way, something like 1014 feet in elevation, and this "1000 feet" continues for some seven miles to Warren. The surrounding region is Glacial Drift, with many undrained prairie marshes, small ponds and with a gently rolling surface. Some five miles to the west, between Nora and Warren, the driftless area is entered. This first section is entirely prairie, and contains some ten restricted areas that may justly be termed "original."

From the margin of the Drift to the vicinity of Apple River, the marginal region of the Driftless Area is passed over. The land is high and rolling, with numerous hollows and from the earliest days, was almost entirely without trees, except along the creeks, with an elevation well above 900 feet. There are some high dry knolls west of the head waters of Clear Creek, with the bed rock but a few feet below the surface. The railway cuts miniature canyons through this limestone.

From Apple River west for some distance, wooded areas occur, succeeded by more open country which culminates in the famous Law's Cut, a mighty gouge in the Maquoketa Shales. Before reaching the cut, the small west branch of Apple River is crossed. This occupies its preglacial channel in a broad flat valley. We are now fairly in the hill land of Mill creek, Hell's Branch and East Fork of the Galena River and down the last named stream, in tortuous course, midst ever heightening hills, the road wends out upon the alluvium of Galena River, past the ancient lead mine city of Galena on its bluffs and slopes and with one last swinging curve out to the bottom lands of the Mississippi.

ILLINOIS STATE ACADEMY OF SCIENCE

From Portage to East Dubuque, the towering bluffs and cliffs are on the right, broken by three river valleys; and to the left, the sloughs, bayous, swamps, bottoms and waters of the great river. So narrow is this strip of land in places that the two other railway lines run their trains over the Illinois Central tracks, there being no room for more. Beyond Portage are many steep wooded slopes abutting on the right of way, numerous ravines, and for some distance, a wonderful palisade of towering lime stone cliffs. After crossing the Little Menominee River, the double tracks separate, the south or east bound passing through the sandy barren before mentioned, joining some two miles east of the western goal. From start to finish, the rails have pursued every direction of the compass except north and east, thus giving every manner of exposure. With the exception of about three miles, the whole distance has been in Jo Daviess Co., and for four miles, just south of the Illinois-Wisconsin Line.

With the above as a working stage, let us investigate the plants of the right of way. The author has a list of 1211 plants found in the county, every part having been repeatedly covered. On the area under consideration, 605 species have been recorded, or exactly one-half lacking one. Truly a remarkable showing.

It may be of interest to tabulate a few groups before considering some of the rarer and more choice forms that here are finding their last hope of existence in the whole county.

There are 110 examples of good and genuine weeds. This is no slander upon the zeal of our section men, for be it known, there is no place like a railway for such an exhibit. Many of these are tramps, pure and simple, and lead a precarious life, season by season, each year with a somewhat different combination. Such are the three wild four o'clocks, (Oxybaphus); numerous spurges (Euphorbia); the lance-leaved sage (Salvia lancifolia); two Chenopodiums, the Jerusalem oak and Mexican tea, the Cotton plant, Silver orach (Atriplex argentea); Flax, rape, turnip, wheat, oats, rye, barley, and alfalfa represent our cultivated plant group. Cow-herb (Vaccaria) is a showy example of a tramp weed.

111

PAPERS ON BIOLOGY AND AGRICULTURE

Among these tramps are a few that cannot be considered weeds, at least with us. The western gum weed or tar weed (Grindelia squarrosa) is found here and there; the showy evening primrose (Oenothera speciosa) rarely occurs; the hoary night-shade (Solanum elaeagnifolium); Froelichia; Scarlet gaura (Gaura coccinea); the wild potato vine (Ipomoea pandurata); Petunia; tomato; hop clover (Trifolium procumbens) are tramp plants of this character.

To summarize further, we find:
  17 ferns
  100 grasses
  70 sedges
  110 weeds
  35 water plants
  100 composites or members of the Aster family
  40 shrubs
  133 other plants
  ———
  605

Fifty-five species of trees adjacent to or leaning over the line fences may be referred to. These cannot perhaps be included in actual right of way plants but would be there but for the hand of man.

The ferns are found almost exclusively on the rocky portions of the right of way from Warren west. The rock brake (Pellaea) is more and more finding such rock cuts congenial dwelling places. Here also, the Woodsia thrives, and the dainty and interesting bulblet fern (Cystopteris). On the great rock-fragments the walking fern is occasional, and the ostrich fern forms small colonies on the low alluvium of creek borders. The flowering fern is at home on shaded banks and the very rare Feei cliff fern (Cheilanthes Feei) is overlooked on sun exposed cliffs.

The grasses and sedges are very abundant on all the marshy and prairie portions, as well as in the shade of the Mississippi bluff woods. There are 53 species of the genus Carex, 10 of Cyperus, 15 of Panicum. The only species that need special mention are wild rice (Zizania); purple love grass (Eragrostis pectinacea); blue joint (Andropogon furcatus); sand-binder grass (Calamovilfa); sand grass (Panicum virgatum) ; the curious drop seed grass (Sporobolus heterolepis) ; the great cord grass (Spartina) ; two mesquite grasses (Bouteloua hirsuta and oligostach-ya) ; and the great Lyme grass (Elymus robustus).

A few water plants or wet marsh forms are worthy of comment. The western water lily; two yellow pond lilies (Nymphaea advena and rubrodisca) ; the yellow and white water crowfoots; an arrow head (Sagittaria latifolia) with a leaf and stalk 6 feet in length; the rare Lophotocarpus calycinus in an isolated flood pond near East Dubuque; five species of yellow and purple bladderworts (Utricularia) ; water willow (Decodon) ; the great swamp rose mallow (Hibiscus militaris) ; the water plantain (Alisma).

Some 12 trees that may with propriety be listed are: the canoe birch on the Mississippi bluffs; the yellow birch on the bottoms; the red cedar on the bald cliffs; at their base, the Kentucky coffee tree; the ashes, green, black, red and white in appropriate soils; the red mulberry on the lower part of the rich wooded slope; the king nut or bottom shagbark hickory on the dry bottoms; the black sugar maple and the rock elm, associates on rocky lowlands.

The shrubs are soon disposed of, for of the many, only a few need attention; the juniper is at home on the cliff-brows; the yellow bush honeysuckle (Diervilla) on the rocky banks; the genuine arrow wood (Viburnum dentatum) and now and then a wild snowball (Viburnum americanum) on a damp cliff; yellow and red honeysuckles are here and there; the shrubby cinquefoil (Potentilla fruticosa) delights in cool damp cliffs, where also the prickly gooseberry, the nine-bark (Physocarpus) and the American yew (Taxus) are to be found. Five species of Cornus or dogwood are often met with, the common one being the small white (Cornus paniculata). In the undrained swamps, buttonbush and many willows grow.

Of the herbaceous plants not included in the above, and numbering some 233 species, there are many very striking forms, a number of which have not been found in Jo Daviess Co. except along the Illinois Central Railway. Let us dispose of these first, without order but as they occur

PAPERS ON BIOLOGY AND AGRICULTURE

from Waddams to East Dubuque. As will be noted, these plants are largely original prairie species.

Between Waddams and Nora are colonies of the palmate, larkspur and birdfoot violets; the early crowfoot (Ranunculus rhomboideus) and the white blue-eyed grass (Sisyrinchium albidum). Between Nora and Warren are many fine examples of the cream colored wild indigo (Baptisia bracteata), the Quamash (Camassia), the wonderful white fringed orchis (Habenaria leucophoea) in a blanket of white on the moist low prairie; the deep blue prairie gentian (Gentiana puberula), the most enduring and bluest of our species; the flesh colored milkwort (Polygala incarnata) ; and the prairie parsley (Polytaenia). Near Apple River is a fine collection of purple coneflowers (Brauneria pallida) ; the prairie dandelion (Agoseris) ; the yellow hop clover, and the spicate blazing star (Liatris spicata). West of Apple River are numbers of cream wild indigo and Valerianella (V. chenopodifolia) ; also great collections of the edible valerian.

Near Galena, by the side of the river, is a great patch of the glade mallow (Napaea), this having been found by the author in but one other locality in Illinois; the showy hedge nettle (Stachys tenuifolia); a red form of oxalis (O. rufa of Britton) always in wet rock cuts; the two colored skullcap (Scutellaria versicolor; Sullivantia and Zygadenus chloranthus or Camass. While found elsewhere, the lilies (L. superbum and philadelphicum) are far finer on the undisturbed soil of the railroad strip. The yellow lady's slipper occurs in many places, the small white form on Apple River only.

Along the stretch of road from Portage to East Dubuque are a number of fine plants. Here only do we find the beautiful Ipomoea before named and the rose mallow; twinflower (Jeffersonia) ; golden Corydalis; the long flowered Puccoon; the striking poppy mallow (Callirhoe involucrata) ; the white plains thistle (Cirsium undulatum) ; C. pumilum, the fragrant one, beloved by country children who plunder it for nectar, extends the whole length; at one place only is the great Rudbeckia (R. subtomentosa) found; the small white milkweed thrives at the

114

western limits, while the showy prairie species (Asclepias sullivantia) abounds at the eastern portion.

Much more might be said but enough has been presented to emphasize strongly the part our great railways, built nearly three-quarters of a century ago, have in conserving and preserving our fast diminishing company of choicer plants. Here many I have named are making their last stand before extinction. It is indeed a pity that some way cannot be found to enable the railroads to set apart here and there choice remnants of this vanishing flora, to be placarded and cared for by state or local societies, as some evidence of "the glory that once was."

In conclusion, I wish to thank the Illinois Central Railway for many courtesies extended in the past days, and for the use of their large scale maps which have been used in making the sectional maps of this paper. The railroad possesses the last rear-guard of the innumerable host of beauties that once made glad the Illinois lands. This is an asset not adding an iota to the dividend of dollars, but which, preserved to the flower-loving public who ride on its trains, will engender in the hearts of an increasing constituency, a kindlier opinion toward a so-called soulless corporation, that is thus able to blend with its great undertakings, a generous and fostering concern for the flower suppliants to be cherished or blasted by its decree.

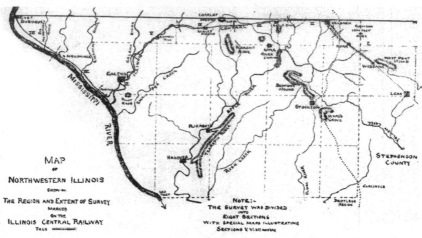

MAP
OF
NORTHWESTERN ILLINOIS
SHOWING
THE REGION AND EXTENT OF SURVEY
MARKED
ON THE
ILLINOIS CENTRAL RAILWAY
THUS

NOTE:—
THE SURVEY WAS DIVIDED
INTO
EIGHT SECTIONS
WITH SPECIAL MAPS ILLUSTRATING
SECTIONS V, VI, VII, VIII

FIG. 1

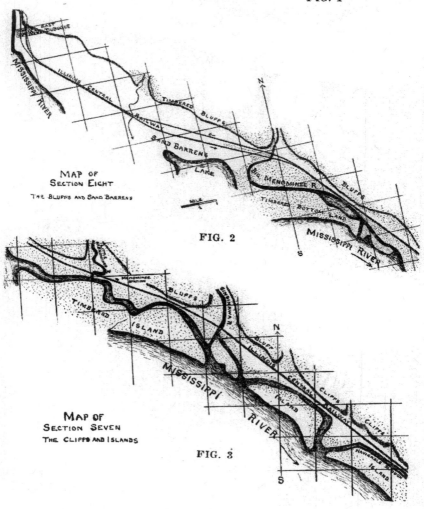

MAP OF
SECTION EIGHT
THE BLUFFS AND SAND BARRENS

FIG. 2

MAP OF
SECTION SEVEN
THE CLIFFS AND ISLANDS

FIG. 3

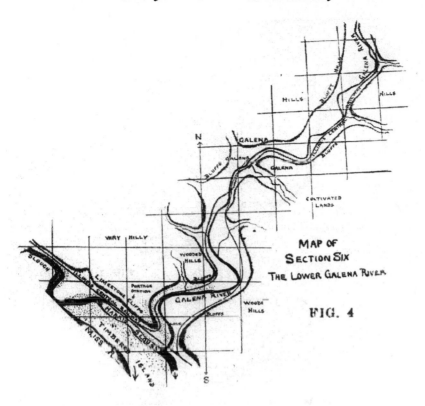

MAP OF
SECTION SIX
THE LOWER GALENA RIVER

FIG. 4

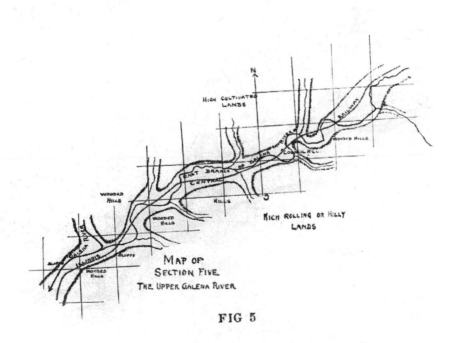

MAP OF
SECTION FIVE.
THE UPPER GALENA RIVER

FIG 5

PRIMULA MISTASSINICA IN ILLINOIS AND IN DISTRIBUTION

This short paper is not intended as an intensive study of this interesting far northern species but to present in condensed form its distribution and more particularly to call to your attention the fact that its southernmost limit appears, for the time at least, to be in northwestern Illinois. If you will consult the map here introduced you will observe dark areas extending from Newfoundland to Yukon territory and from Ungava and Great Slave lake to Illinois and New York. These shaded spots show centers of occurrence, often of some considerable size, or again as in the Illinois marking, but a half square mile where the plant if found. The territory of distribution is, therefore some 2500 miles from east to west and 1200 miles from north to south.

It must be understood that large sections of country often separate these centers that have no records of occurrence. For example in the variety Primula mistassinica noveboracensis the next station eastwardly in the belt of occupation is in mid Michigan some 250 miles away and the next step takes us well into southern Ontario. There may be undiscovered stations but as far as Illinois and lower Michigan are concerned the list appears complete.

The systematists have divided this <u>Primula</u> into two
well marked varieties and a color form; <u>Primula mistassini</u>
<u>typica</u> Michx., <u>Primula mistassinica noveboracensis</u> Fernald
and <u>forma leucantha</u> Fernald. The species, its name derive
from Lake Mistassina in northeastern Quebec, a situation
by the way where it is not found, extends from Labrador to
Yukon territory and south through the Canadian provinces
to British Columbia and Alberta on the west, northern
Minnesota, Wisconsin, Michigan at the center, Vermont,
Maine and New Brunswick on the east. Its principal
distinguishing characters besides the small size and lack
of mealiness is the marked yellow eye of the flower.

The <u>**forma** leucantha</u> is found centered in eastern
Quebec and has white flowers. The variety <u>noveboracensis</u>
is the one the United States is most concerned with as it

120

occupies a long band extending from eastern and southern New York through south Ontario, south Michigan and a last huge jump into Jo Daviess county, Illinois. This variety is in every way smaller and lacks almost entirely the yellow eye of the flower. The "farthest south," is the Illinois station 6 miles south of parallel of latitude 42' 30", the north boundary of Illinois. The New York stations are a few miles further north.

The testimony seems to make it plain that the type and not the variety is the form found in upper Michigan, upper Wisconsin and in Minnesota. The single Iowa mutation has not been investigated.

The author has ransacked the land from Alberta to Quebec and from Iowa to Rhode Island seeking good photographs of this interesting plant but has finally been compelled to use his own rather indefinite ones, which are are now

shown as lantern slides. ~~None of these show the leaves.~~
~~Huron H. Smith but two days before his tragic death sent a~~
~~photograph from Milwaukee which also does not show the leaves.~~

[Pepoon's Lantern Slide of Bird's Eye Primrose on the Cliffs at Apple
River Canyon. (Added in 2011 by Editor. Source: Chicago Academy of Sciences)]

The Primrose rocks of Jo Daviess county and of the
newest of our state parks, Apple River Canyon park are a
limited number of limestone cliffs mostly on the west
branch of Apple river a quarter of a mile above the junction
of the two branches of the head of the canyon at the place
where ninety years ago was the thriving village of Millville.

These cliffs have a west and northwest exposure, are
about sixty to seventy-five feet high, made up of Galena
dolmitic limestone. The base of the cliff is constantly
wet with dripping water and does not ordinarily freeze.
The primrose band is about ten feet in vertical elevation

and some hundreds of feet long at the place of greatest
abundance.

The cliff since its discovery on April 29, 1908 has
become quite a mecca for botanical zealots and collectors.
One confessed, after the deed was done, that he had
abstracted four hundred four complete flowering plants
but he said, "without making any noticeable impression on
the number."

In concluding this brief account I append the statements
of those who so kindly assisted in furnishing the data
necessary to the completion of the paper. The thanks are in
an especial degree tended to Professor M. L. Fernald of
Harvard who supplied so much information, to Dr. Malte,
Chief Botanist National Herbarium, Ottawa, Canada, who
contributed the map of Canada and to Father Louis-Marie
LaLonde, University of Montreal, La Trappe, Quebec, Canada,
who sent actual specimens from Quebec. I also wish to
thank Professor M. C. Taylor, University of Toronto, Canada,
who reports specimens from Port Arthur, Collingwood. Southampton,
Elora and Banff, " a calciphile in the region about the
Great Lakes." Father Marie-Victorin, University of Montreal
Canada reports, "Primula mistassinica was discovered by
Michaux at Lake Mistassini. Of frequent occurrence all around
the Gulf of St. Lawrence, coming as far west as the Island
of Orleans, near the city of Quebec. Absent in the Montreal
district, in the alluvial plain, and in the Laurentides

generally, except in the far north reappearing in the
Bruce peninsula." Professor W. A. Anderson, University of
Iowa reports one station in central part of state.
Professor John Davidson, University of British Columbia, Canada
reports no specimens from British Columbia. Professor
Norman Fassett, University of Wisconsin and Professor
J. H. Ehlers, University of Michigan have also contributed
information.

Professor Fernald speaks of variety <u>noveboracensis</u>:

"Var. <u>noveboracensis</u> has smaller flowers than
most of the more northern and typical P. <u>mistassinica</u>
but occasional northern plants have them as small.
In its lack of a well marked orange eye it is most
striking, true P. <u>mistassinica</u> having the throat
bordered by a brilliant yellow or orange ring (as in
most of the <u>Farinosae</u>). The leaves of var.
<u>noveboracensis</u> are somewhat distinctive but similar
foliage occasionally occurs in the more northern
type with larger corolla and yellow eye."

H. S. Pepoon
Natural History Survey
University of Illinois
Urbana, Illinois

PEPOON SCRAPBOOK.

RECITATION HALL.
WARREN ACADEMY.

Pepoon's boyhood school in Warren, IL.

HERM PEPOON'S POEMS

Of all the boys in High school, Herm Pepoon was thought to be the most faithful to the rules and studies. We emulated him. He was our pattern. Little did we imagine that, while apparently engrossed in study, he was concocting poems. The following were given to a certain young lady, who has preserved them for this appearance. They are now printed to show, not only "that murder will out," but so that we may all know what kind of a boy Herm was. He had 200 pounds of good nature.

*   *   *   *   *

THE VILLAGE SCHOOLMASTER

In the pleasant village, Warren
　Is the Warren High School building.
And the teacher, D. E. Garver,
　Is a man of much importance
'Mongst the Warren High School Scholars
　And his voice is stern and frightful
When he see'eth scholars whisper.
　And he sayeth "Look you careful
Five per cent for every whisper,
　When 'tis sixty to Directors
Go you fast as you can go there.
　I have given you timely warning,
Profit by it." And he sinks back blandly
　In his chair behind the organ,
And his sterness goes from out him.
　　　　　　　—H. S. Pepoon.

*   *   *   *   *

Excerpt from Warren School's History expressing reverence for Pepoon, even at a young age, and introducing his nickname, "Herm."

THE DESERTED VILLAGE

On the fertile western prairie,
　In the state of Illinois,

In the county of Jo Daviess,
　By the rushing Apple River,
Lies the pleasant village Millville,
　Once a village of importance
Was it, when its streets resounded
　With political discussion,
With the sound of sledge and anvil,
　With the creaking of the mill wheel,
With the tongues of busy people.
　And the scenery round about it.
On the banks of Apple River,
　By the rushing muddy water,
Was most gorgeous to contemplate.
　And the rocks in shape were varied;
Here a rock of huge dimensions,
　There a most fantastic figure
With a multitude of angles,
　With its sides and summit covered
With the stunted pine and cedar
　In whose boughs the hawk had builded
Nest of rush and twigs together,
　As a place to rear her nestlings
Hidden from the eyes of boyhood.
　Perched upon its topmost branches,
Saw the wild duck fly below her,
　And, with velocity of lightning,
With the speed of musket bullet,
　Swooped she downward from her eyrie,
And had seized her prey before it
　Was acquainted of her coming.
This and more could be seen daily
　By the lover of the beauteous,
By the student of Dame Nature,
　On the banks of Apple River,
Round the pleasant village Millville
　In the bright days of her greatness.
Past is all her former glory!
　Past is all her boasted greatness!
And her name has sunk to nothing,
　In the catalogue of cities,
In the history of the nation.

　　　　　　　—H. S. Pepoon.

The Deserted Village, written in high school, describes the former town of Millville, the future site of Apple River Canyon State Park.

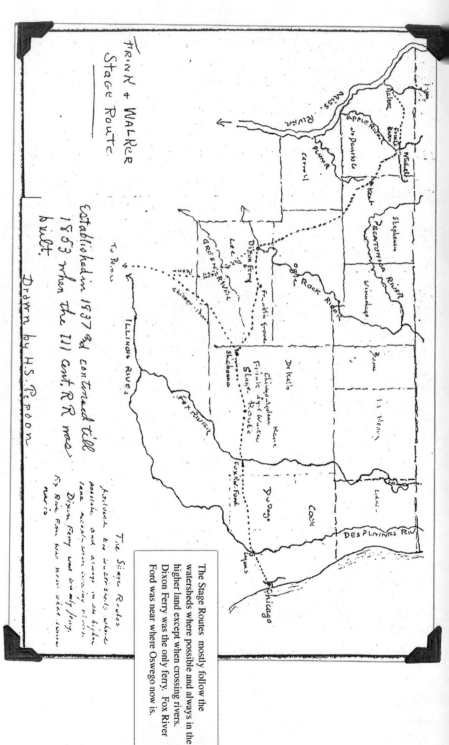

Early map drawn by Pepoon showing the famed Frink and
Walker Stagecoach Route. The date is unknown.

The Stage Routes mostly follow the
watersheds where possible and always in the
higher land except when crossing rivers.
Dixon Ferry was the only ferry. Fox River
Ford was near where Oswego now is.

618   THE AMERICAN BEE JOURNAL.   *Sept. 24,*

PLANTS TO BE NAMED.

By DR. H. S. PEPOON,
936 Belleplaine Ave., Station X, Chicago, Ill.

Ready for Business.

I have been absent on a camping tour, and have only lately returned to the city. This will be my excuse for past delays in answering queries about plants. I am ready now, however, to attend strictly to business, so send them on.

H. S. PEPOON.

Partridge-Pea—Water Hore-Hound.

I send two different plants, which I would like to have named. They grow around here on low sandy lands. Do you know anything about their honey-producing qualities?   A. V. R.
De Motte, Ind., Aug. 6.

ANSWER.—No. 1, is the partridge-pea spoken of in a former number of the Bee Journal.

No. 2, is a member of the mint family, and has the common name of water-hore-hound, (botanically *lycopus*). Like many mints it is well supplied with honey, and seems a favorite with the smaller bees.

Willow-Herb.

I enclose a sample of flower that made its first appearance here last summer. The marshes are fairly covered with them. What is its name, and how does it rank as a honey-producer?
Hancock, Wis., June 27.   S. R. H.

ANSWER.—The plant you send is the willow-herb, already treated of in the Bee Journal for July.

Bush Clover.

I enclose a plant whose name I wish to know. Does it produce much honey? My bees are now working on it all day long, and we have oceans of it here.
Albertville, Ala., Aug. 26.   J. H. S.

ANSWER.—The plant you send is a *hespedeza*, common name "clover," belonging to the Pulse family, already often mentioned as containing the clovers and other honey-plants. As to the honey-producing qualities I can say nothing. In the North the genus is not apparently a valuable one for honey, but experience may prove that some of the species have merit.

Partridge-Pea—Figwort.

I send two plants. Will you kindly give me their names? No. 1, some call "buttercup." It grows to perfection on low ground, on the banks of ditches and roadside. No. 2, I know no common name for. I only know one patch—it is

NOW WE HAVE IT!

GLEASON'S ✠✠✠✠✠ HORSE-BOOK!

The Only Complete and Authorized Work by America's King of Horse-Trainers,

PROF. OSCAR R. GLEASON,

Renowned throughout America and recognized by the United States Government as the most expert and successful horseman of the age. The whole work comprises History, Breeding, Training, Breaking, Buying, Feeding, Grooming, Shoeing, Doctoring, Telling Age, and General Care of the Horse.

You will know all about a horse after you have read it.

No one can fool you on the age of a horse after you have read it.

Prof. Gleason subduing "Black Devil," the man-eating stallion, at Philada., Pa.

Prof. Gleason has drawn larger crowds than the great P. T. Barnum, with his big show, ever did

416 Octavo Pages—173 Striking Illustrations.

Produced under the direction of the U. S. Government Veterinary Surgeon.

In this book Prof. Gleason has given to the world for the first time his most wonderful methods of training and treating horses.

100,000 SOLD AT $3.00 EACH.

But we have arranged to supply a limited number of copies to our subscribers **absolutely free.** First come, first served.

Here are Our Offers of this Great Book.

Pepoon had a frequent column, "Plants to be Named," in the *American Bee Journal* during 1896.

EXPLOSION IN LABORATORY INJURES HIGH SCHOOL GIRL.

Acid Thrown on Arm of Miss Mamie Peterson—Instructor in Charge Says Accident Is No One's Business.

Miss Mamie Peterson, a fourth year pupil in the Lake View High School, received a painful burn yesterday as the result of an explosion in the chemical laboratory of the school. With a number of her classmates she was manufacturing hydro-sulphurous acid. It is thought some water was permitted to run into the generator and caused it to boil over and explode. A quantity of the acid struck Miss Peterson's arm, inflicting a severe burn from the elbow nearly to the hand. The accident caused some excitement in the school, and exaggerated reports reached the different rooms.

One of Miss Peterson's companions summoned Dr. Herman S. Pepoon, instructor of biology and a physician. He says she will be able to resume her school work in a few days.

Dr. Pepoon said last evening: "It is regretable that such an accident should have occurred, and I believe one of the pupils must have been careless. It is the first accident at the Lake View High School in ten years. I do not know who was in charge of the class at the time. When I reached the laboratory I found Mr. Linebarger there."

Charles E. Linebarger, who has charge of the chemical laboratory at the school, said last night: "It's nobody's business if one of the pupils was burned in the laboratory. The burn was only a slight one, and such minor burns are received in the laboratory every week. They cannot interest the public."

While teaching at Lakeview High School Pepoon served as the school physician. This story explains Pepoon's role helping a student injured in Chemistry lab and an unusual response by the lab's instructor.

DESTRUCTION OF A FARM FLORA.
By H. S. Pepoon.

I HAVE been much interested in the movement that seems to be gathering added force as the months go by, and that has for its object the preservation of our wild plants. It certainly will receive my hearty cooperation in every possible way, the more so because I live in the midst of a people who are waging the most relentless war of extermination against a number of the most beautiful of our native orchids and lilies. It might surprise the reader to learn that I have seen 300 showy lady-slippers (*Cypripedium reginae*) gathered by a thoughtless trio in two hours' time; but so it is, and these plants are now numbered by tens when five years ago they were in troops of hundreds.

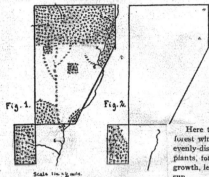

Fig. 1.   Fig. 2.

Scale 1in = ½ mile.

Fig. 1. A farm of 226 acres in 1876. The years of death of woodland, 2 springs, and a living stream. The farm contains ...

Fig. 2. The same farm in 1904. There are only 18 acres of woodland, no springs, and no stream. The plants number only 200 species, 155 having been exterminated in 28 years.

Here the destroying factor has doubtless been the removal of the forest with its kindly influence in affording shelter and plentiful and evenly-distributed moisture. A similar fate awaits, I fear, all forest plants, for man seems determined to clear the earth of trees of natural growth, leaving it bare and desolate under the fierce heat of our summer sun.

In this same time it may be of interest to relate the history of my old home farm in northwestern Illinois. It was a woodland originally—with several "sloughs" as we called them—low-lying ravines or small valleys, very wet along the lowest level, running through from north to south. The woodlands were oak—with many "flat openings" near the heads of the ravines. The soil varied from a rich black loam in the heavy timber to a thin clay on the hillsides. Every hollow had a spring, and the main valley always possessed a fine running stream. This was at a time when 120 acres of the 226 were in forest growths.

My "mouth waters" as I think of those days. The rich woods were full of red baneberry, blue cohosh, may-apples, spikenard, ginseng, shin-leaf, tway-blade, pogonia, bracted and showy orchids, yellow and showy lady-slippers, wild yams, solomon's seal, bellwort, trilliums, and jack-in-the-pulpits. Not *one* of these plants is now found on the farm. Gone they are, with the trees they loved.

To refer to what some reader may believe to be a sad blunder on my part, viz., the showy lady-slipper in rich moist woodlands: The books say in "bogs, etc."; but, alas, the books are often at fault, for in northwestern Illinois these plants *always* grew in woods, or on hillsides or bluffs. Here about Chicago they behave according to the books, but not there. The beautiful calopogon had the same unconventional way—growing only on bald bluffs. In the woods with thin soil grew asters, shin-leaves, violets, lousewort, painted cups. In the "flat openings" were found wild indigo, "pennyroyal," as we called it (the Koellia of to-day), pink polygalas, purple guardias. The "sloughs" (pronounced "slew") yielded turks-caps and meadow lilies, marsh bellwort, button snake-root, closed gentian and pussy-willows galore.

All are gone. I have a list made out in 1876 enumerating 355 plants on that famed farm. To-day there are barely 200, and these are the "plebeians" and "toughs," "tramps" and "rabble" of the plant world. The royal ones are all missing.

1	Clematis virginiana	22½	2	Trifolium pratense
2	Anemone pennsylvanica	23	3	T. repens
3	A. virginiana		4	Amphicarpa monoica
4	A. nemorosa		5	Petalostemon violaceus
5	Thalictrum purpurascens		53	P. candidus
7	T. polygamum		58	Robinia viscosa
8	Ranunculus rhomboideus	59		Astragalus canadensis
9	R. abortivus		59	Desmodium acuminatum
10	R. fascicularis		60	D. viridiflorum
11	R. septentrionalis	24	61	D. canadense
12	Caltha palustris		62	Lespedeza capitata
13	Actea rubra		65	Amorpha canescens
14	Menispermum canadense	25	26	Prunus americana
15	Caulophyllum thalictroides		67	P. pennsylvanica
16	Podophyllum peltatum		68	P. virginiana
17	Cardamine rhomboidea	27	69	P. serotina
18	Nasturtium palustre		70	Physocarpus opulifolius
19	Sisymbrium officinale		71	Spiraea salicifolia
20	Capsella bursa-pastoris		72	Rubus strigosus
21	Lepidium virginicum	25	73	R. occidentalis
22	Brassica nigra		74	R. villosus
			75	R. canadensis
23	Viola ...		76	Geum album
24	Helianthemum canadense	30	77	Fragaria virginiana
25	Viola pedatifida	31	78	Potentilla arguta
26	V. cucullata		79	P. norvegica
27	V. sagittata	32	80	P. canadensis
28	Saponaria vaccaria	33	81	Agrimonia eupatoria
29	Lychnis githago		82	Rosa lucida
30	Arenaria lateriflora		83	R. carolina
31	Cerastium vulgatum		84	R. humilis
32	Portulaca oleracea		85	Pyrus coronaria
33	Hypericum maculatum		86	Pyrus malus
34	Malva rotundifolia		87	Crataegus coccinea
35	Linum sulcatum		88	C. tomentosa
36	Geranium maculatum		91	Saxifraga pennsylvanica
37	Oxalis violacea		92	Heuchera hispida
38	O. stricta		93	Parnassia caroliniana
39	Xanthoxylum americanum		94	Penthorum sedoides
40	Celastrus scandens		95	Lythrum alatum
41	Euonymus atropurpureus		96	Ludwigia palustris
42	Ceanothus americanus		97	Epilobium coloratum
43	Vitis aestivalis		98	Oenothera biennis
44	V. riparia		99	Gaura
	V. cordifolia		100	Circaea lutetiana
45	Ampelopsis quinquefolia		101	Thaspium aureum
46	Rhus glabra		102	Cryptotaenia canadensis
47	R. toxicodendron		103	Berula angustifolia
48	Polygala verticillata		104	Cicuta maculata
49	P. senega		105	Osmorrhiza longistylis
50	P. sanguinea		106	O. brevistylis
51	Baptisia leucantha			

A personal copy of Pepoon's *Destruction of a Farm Flora* with an accompanying list of plant species.

THE THREE BOTANISTS
Taken in 1909

The Three Botanists (From Left: Herman Pepoon, William
James Beal (1833 – 1924), Levi M. Umbach (1853 – 1918)).

HERMON S. PEPOON, M.D. the "Poet"

of 1876-'77

Photo of 1918

1918 picture showing the former Warren High School "Poet."

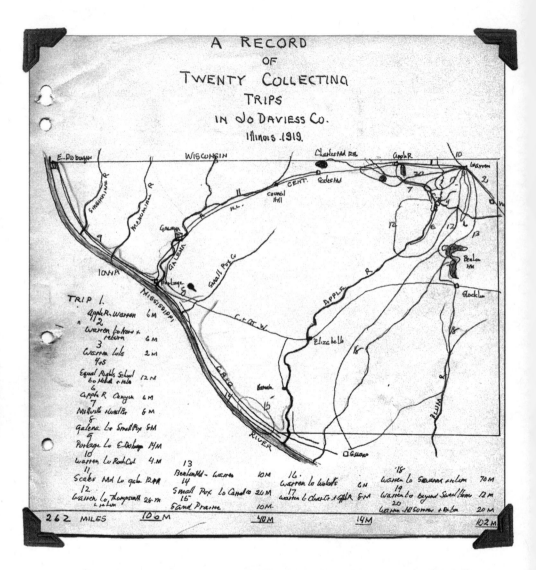

Meticulous record keeping shows Pepoon's trampings through Jo Daviess County in 1919: 262 miles!

...other...be inherited a larger share of...immense estate.

...remony was followed by a wedding breakfast, at which the families and about fifty intimate friends were present.

After their honeymoon Mr. and Mrs. Ream will return to New York, where they will make their future home.

* *

Prairie Club Hike.

Members of the Prairie club will walk this afternoon from Edgebrook to Morton Grove, leaving on the Chicago, Milwaukee and St. Paul (Union station) at 2:05 p. m. Dr. H. S. Pepoon, instructor in biology at Lake View High school, will give a lecture on the natural history of the district.

Wild Flower Society.

The Illinois chapter of the Wild Flower Preservation society will hold its annual meeting and spring luncheon at noon today at the Woman's City club. Dr. H. S. Pepoon will give an illustrated talk on "Beauty Spots and Plants of Illinois."

OCEAN STEAMSHIP MOVEMENTS.

Arrived.	At.	From.
Ile de France...	Plymouth	... New York
Resolute	...... Kobe	New York
Washington	.... Hamburg ...	New York

Sailed.	From.	For.
Amer. Trader...	New York...	London
Albert Ballin...	Southampton.	New York
Europa	...... Bremen	New York
Georgic	....	New York... Liverpool
Mauretania	.... New York....	Southampton
Pres. Roosevelt..	Southampt'n.	New York
Westernland	..... Antwerp	New York
Vulcania	.... New York...	Naples
Habana	.........New York...	Vigo

TABLET HONORS WAR NURSE WHO GAVE HER LIFE

A Chicago heroine of the world war was honored Saturday when a memor-

LUCILE PEPOON.

ial tablet was dedicated for Miss Lucile Pepoon, a nurse who died while in France. The tablet was placed in Independence park near a tree planted a year ago in her memory. It is several hundred feet from the home of her parents, Dr. and Mrs. Herman S. Pepoon of 3842 Byron street. Before volunteering for service Miss Pepoon was in the bureau of medical inspection of the health department. Dr. H. O. Jones, assistant chief of the bureau, presided at the exercises yesterday, and the dedicatory talk was given by Dr. Heman Spalding, chief of the bureau. Short talks were given by the Rev. A. S. Haskins and Dr. John Dill Robertson.

Article honoring Pepoon's daughter Lucile, who died while serving in France during World War I.

SEVENTEEN PLANT COLLECTING TRIPS IN Jo DAVIESS COUNTY 1919

DATE	TRIP	FROM	TO WHERE	MILES	PLANTS	BLOOMING
	1 F	APPLE RIVER -	WARREN	6		
	2 F	WARREN -	NORA	4		
	3 F	STREETS OF	WARREN	2		
	4 F	EQUAL RIGTS TO	MILLVILLE	3		
	5 F					
	6 F	APPLE RIVER -	CANYON	3		
	7 F	MILLVILLE AND	WEST BRANCH	6		
	8 F	GALENA	TO SMALL POX	8		
	9 F	PORTAGE "	E. DUBUQUE	14		
	10 F	WARREN -	ROCK CUT	4		
	11 F	COUNCIL HILL -	SCALES MD	6		
	12 F	WARREN -	THOMPSON + BACK	33		
	13 F	J.Ts VIA BENTON MD	TO E.RIGTS	10		
	14 F	SMALL POX TO	CARROLL CO LINE	20		
	15 F	SAND PRAIRIE -	HERE + THERE	10		
	16 F	WARREN - WOLF CR	TO WOLCOTTS	6		
	17 F	CLEAR CR TO	APPLE R	5		
	18 HW	WARREN TO SAVANNA + RETNA		70		
	19 F	WARREN -	TO BEYOND SWEETLAND	10		
	20 H.W	WARREN -	MT SUMNER + RET	20		

Species lists from Pepoon's botanizing trips in Jo Daviess County, indicating where plant species were found. These records are invaluable to ecologists today.

THE FRUITS OF THE CHICAGO MARKET

INCLUDING EVERY NATIVE AND IMPORTED FRUIT.

WITH ILLUSTRATIONS AND NOTES

FOUND IN THE

FRUIT AND GROCERY MARKETS FROM SEPT.1 TO DEC.26

OBSERVED BY H.S. PEPOON

KUMQUATS

PEACH   1922   PLUM

An interesting notebook of information and illustrations on Chicago Market fruits, highlighting Pepoon's diverse interest in botany.

Woods *and* Waters *by* BOB BECKER

AN INVITATION TO OUTDOORLOVERS.

EVERY outdoor fan [and this includes the bird student as well as the fisherman] will find it mighty profitable and interesting to visit the fourth annual exhibition now being staged by the Wild Flower Preservation society, the Audubon society and the State Microscopical society at the Art Institute. The exhibits include fish, both native and tropical, bird studies from life, as well as many interesting botanical displays. All the exhibits are open to the public and if you are interested you are welcome.

Not only are there exhibits for you to inspect and study if you wish, but the program also includes lectures on a variety of subjects ranging from mushrooms to migratory birds. As a sample of the lectures we might mention that today two well known Iowa students, Mrs. Charles L. Hutchinson and Dr. H. S. Pepoon, are going to lecture on the "posies" of this region and on Thursday afternoon Frank M. Woodruff, curator of the Academy of Sciences, is going to talk on "The Hoppers and Crawlers in Illinois." Frank has been making a study of snakes and other crawlers and he has a fascinating talk on them.

Every Monday, Thursday and Saturday afternoon from now until Jan. 17 you can drop into the institute and hear a lecture on some phase of outdoor life and our tip is—better take in some of 'em if you care anything about the outdoors.

Nebraska Basket Season Opens with Badger Game

Lincoln, Neb., Dec. 18.—Nebraska university basketball team will open the season with a game played at Madison, Jan. 4, with University of Wisconsin, Director of Athletics Luehring announced today.

Newspaper article promoting one of Pepoon's many
talks to the Wild Flower Preservation Society.

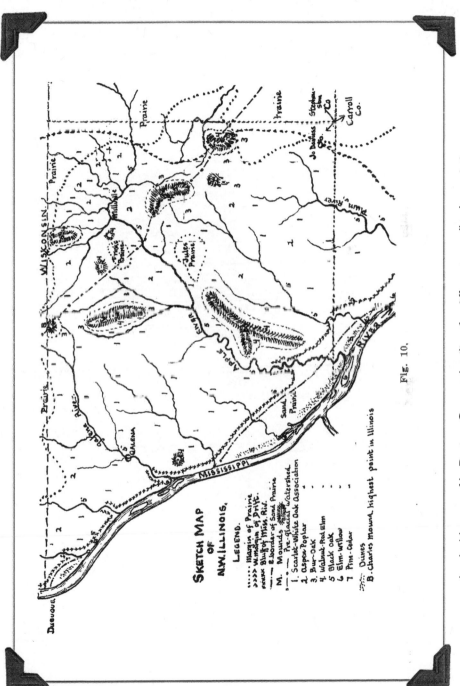

A valuable map of Jo Daviess County detailing the different woodland associations.

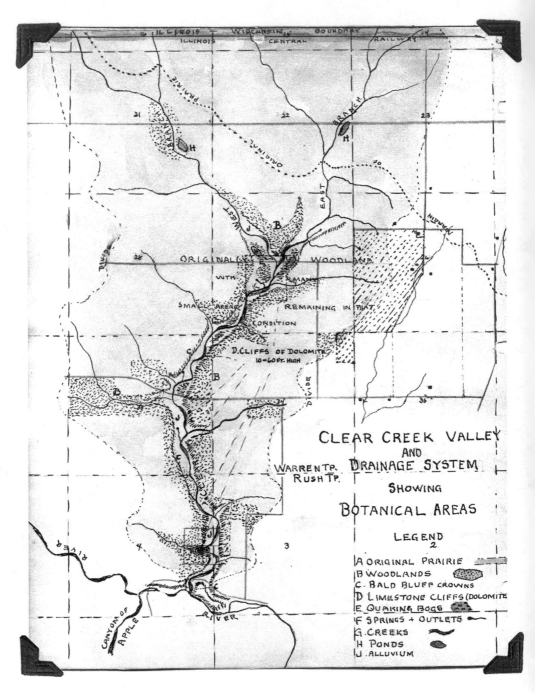

Sketch map showing the landscape features within the Clear Creek Valley watershed, located in western Warren and eastern Rush Townships.

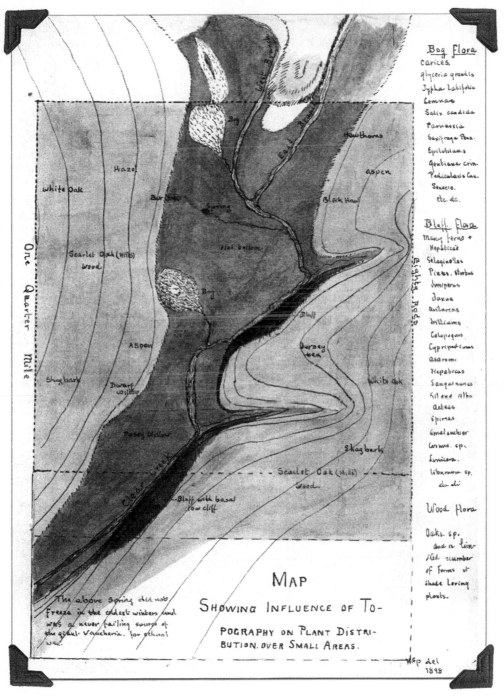

Sketch map of local plant distribution over the changes in topography within the Clear Creek basin, as delineated in 1898.

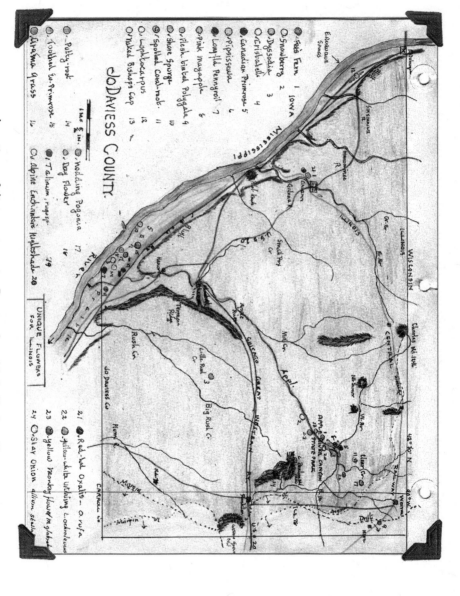

Locations of the rarest species Pepoon found in Jo Daviess County.

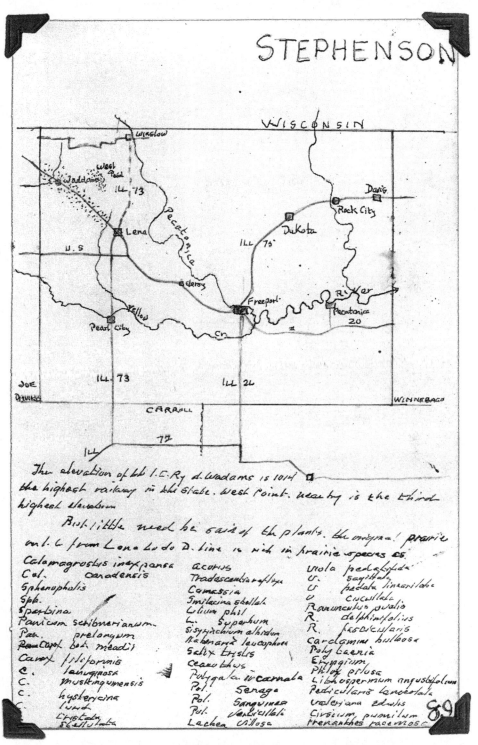

STEPHENSON

WISCONSIN

Winslow

West Point

Waddams

Ill. 73

Davis

Rock City

Pecatonica

Lena

Dakota

U.S.

Ill. 75

McCoy

Freeport

Yellow

River

Pecatonica 20

Pearl City

Cr.

JOE DAVIESS

Ill. 73

Ill. 26

WINNEBAGO

CARROLL

Ill. 77

The elevation of the I.C. Ry. at Wadams is 1014 the highest railway in the state. West Point, nearby is the third highest elevation.

But little need be said of the plants. the original prairie on I.C. from Lena to do D. line is rich in prairie species as.

Calamagrostis inexpansa
Cal. canadensis
Sphenopholis
Sph.
Spartina
Panicum scribnerianum.
Pan. prelongum
Poa Capil bot meadii
Carex filiformis
C. lanuginosa
C. muskingumensis
C. hystericina
lurd
cristata
stellulata

Acorus
Tradescantia reflexa
Camassia
Smilacina stellata
Lilium phil
L. Syperbum
Sisyrinchium albidum
Habenaria leucophaea
Salix Crystris
Ceanothus
Polygala incarnata
Pol. Senega
Pol. Sanguinea
Pol. Verticillata
Lachea villosa

Viola pedatifida
U. Sagittata
U. pedata lineariloba
U. Cucullata
Ranunculus ovalis
R. delphinifolius
R. fascicularis
Cardamine bulbosa
Poly taenia
Eryngium
Phlox pilosa
Lithospermum angustifolium
Pedicularis lanceolata
Valeriana edulis
Cirsium pumilum
Prenanthes racemosa

Map of Stephenson County with and lists the prairie species found along the Illinois Central route.

143

Photos of Apple River Canyon, the top one includes descriptions of Apple River's former location.

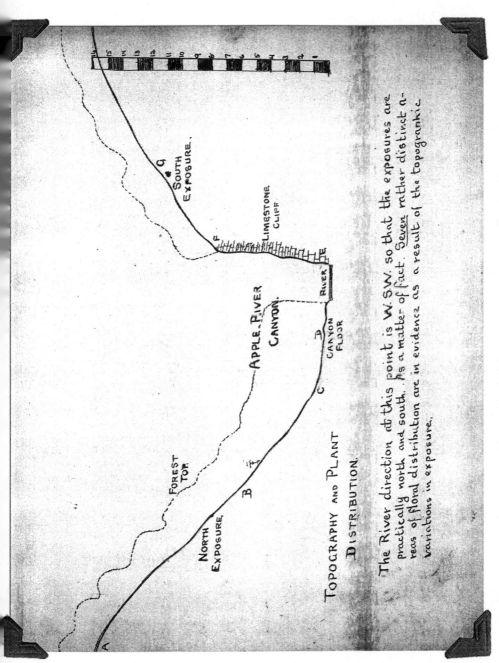

Cross section of Apple River Canyon and the topographical factors that influence its plant distribution.

Society to Preserve Wild Flowers Meets

Mrs. Charles L. Hutchinson, president of the Chicago chapter of the Wild Flower Preservation Society of America, will speak this afternoon at 4 o'clock at the clubroom in the Art Institute on "Wild Flowers You Should Know; Wild Flowers Which Need Protection." Dr. H. S. Pepoon, also will speak on "Comparison in Flower Construction." These are the first of a series of illustrated talks to be given during the fourth annual exhibition of nature studies, which opened on Saturday and will continue through Jan. 18, under the auspices of the preservation society, the Illinois Audubon society and the State Microscopical Society of Illinois.

NEWS OF CHICAGO

* *

Inspecting Apple River.

Do you know where Apple river is? If not, you must ask some member of that lively and peripatetic body, The Friends of Our Native Landscape. They know, because about forty of them explored the banks and braes of Apple river (What is a brae?) a week ago. Under the leadership of Jens Jensen, president of the Friends of O. N. L., and with the assistance of Prof. Pepoon of the Warren High school, the enterprising forty forded and reforded this rustic stream.

They first took a train to Warren, an ancient village in Joe Daviess county. From there they started out and made a six mile hike to a certain spot on the river where the miniature canyon, for which the district is famous, widened out so that the company could establish itself on one side while the performers, who provide the dramatic entertainments at these hikes, could stage on the other side of the stream a presentation of Kenneth Sawyer Goodman's "Masque," a ceremony which takes place every year. There was also much made of lighting the huge bonfire which is a feature of those occasions.

The especial object of this hike was to inspect the Apple River canyon with a view to recommending that it be made a state park. The Friends of O. N. L. have been helpful in promoting the forest park preserves in various localities. They are old habitués and lovers of the Dunes, and have at one time and another tramped over many of Illinois' picturesque districts.

* *

Inspecting Apple River, an article from 1921, explains the pilgrimage of members of the Friends of Our Native Landscape to Apple River Canyon and a Kenneth Sawyer Goodman Masque that was performed.

Prairie Club. McHoile 1918

Helen

The Po... in arms Apple River
Prairie Club

Pictures from The Prairie Club's outing to the canyon in 1918.

Apple River

THE PRIMROSE CLIFFS OF ILLINOIS

Discovered by H.S. Pepoon in 1909.

Picture of the cliffs that harbor the Bird's Eye Primrose plants. Date Unknown.

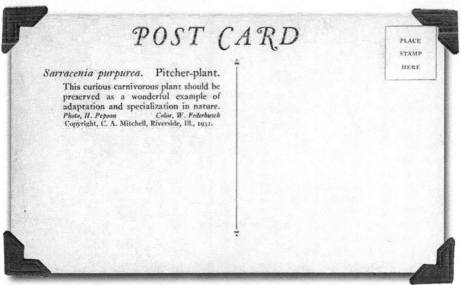

POST CARD

Sarracenia purpurea. Pitcher-plant.

This curious carnivorous plant should be preserved as a wonderful example of adaptation and specialization in nature.
Photo, H. Pepoon   *Color, W. Federbusch*
Copyright, C. A. Mitchell, Riverside, Ill., 1932.

PLACE
STAMP
HERE

A picture of Pitcher Plant (*Sarracenia purpurea*) taken by Pepoon. It was later colorized and sold as a postcard.

FLORA
of the Chicago Region

H. S. PEPOON

The cover of *Flora of the Chicago Region*, published in 1927.

AN ANNOTATED FLORA OF THE CHICAGO AREA

With Maps and Many Illustrations from Photographs of Topographic and Plant Features.

By H. S. PEPOON, B.S., M.D., Head Instructor in Botany and Agriculture, Lake View High School.

CHICAGO, ILLINOIS
1927

The title page from *Flora of the Chicago Region.*

A journal listing the flora of Jo Daviess County as identified in 1939. A joy
to page through today!

Lake View High School

Chicago Herald Examiner 5/22/1930

"GOOD-BY AND GOOD LUCK!"—

Jane Emery, pupil of Lake View High School, leads
her fellow pupils in bidding farwell to Dr. Herman S.
Pepoon, for thirty-seven years an instructor in botany
at the school, as he is automatically retired at the age
of 70.

Herald and Examiner phot

Photograph of Lakeview
High School and a clipping
about Pepoon's retirement.

TELLS HOW BEDS OF LOTUS SPRANG UP OVER ILLINOIS

Residents in the vicinity of the Fox lake chain, in western Lake county, have long boasted that the lotus beds in Grass lake are the only ones growing outside Egypt.

Dr. H. S. Pepoon, of the Illinois natural history survey, overturned this contention yesterday in a speech before the Illinois conservation council at the Morrison hotel.

"The Fox lake beds are probably the oldest in Illinois," he said, "and it is likely the Indians used the roots and the seeds for food. But there are beds in backwaters of the Illinois river southwest of Ottawa, one in Putnam county and others in Thompson lake and Rice lake, Fulton county."

It was the theory of Dr. Pepoon that seeds from the Fox lake plants floated down the river and established colonies in new locations. The lotus seed, he said, would maintain its fertility for a century.

A summary about a presentation given by Pepoon, while a botanist for the Illinois Natural History Survey, on the history of Lotus beds in Grass Lake.

PEPOON, BARRETT MAKE PLANT STUDY IN CHICAGO

Dr. H. S. Pepoon, assistant botanist for the State Natural History
survey and his assistant, Everett
Barrett, are in Chicago where they
are classifying and inspecting the
plants of this state which are dis-
played in the Field museum. This
work is in preparation for a publication to be written in the near future on the flora of Illinois.

A clipping from The Daily Illini (1932) describing a book that never materialized.

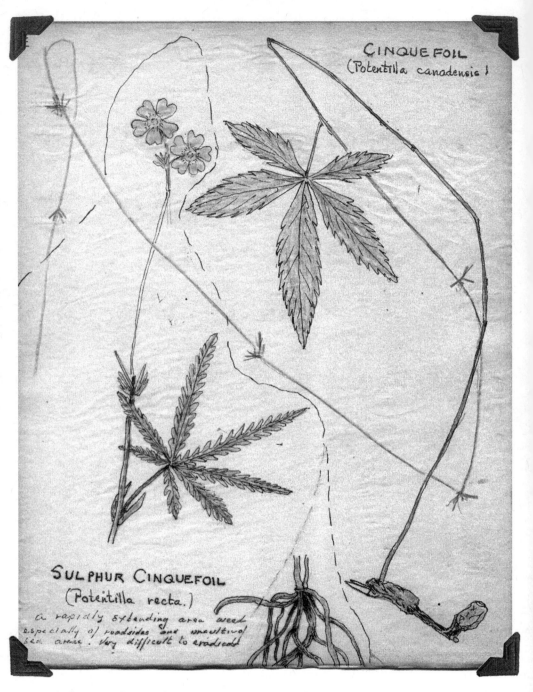

A drawing of native *Potentilla canadensis* next to non-native *Potentilla recta*, which includes Pepoon's early description of an invasive species.

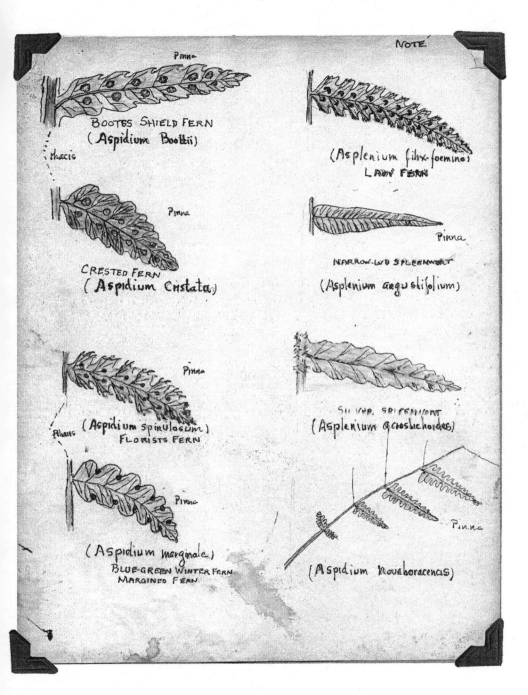

Sketches of several Illinois fern species depicting identifying features.

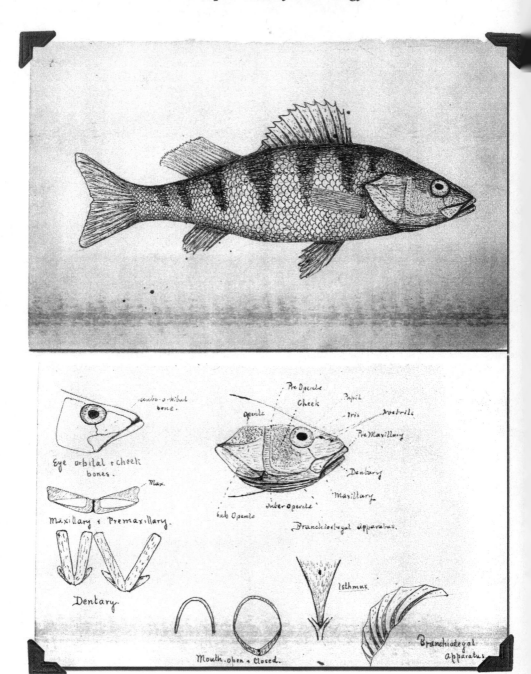

An illustration of Yellow Perch (*Perca flavescens*) that displays Pepoon's passion as a naturalist and as an artist.

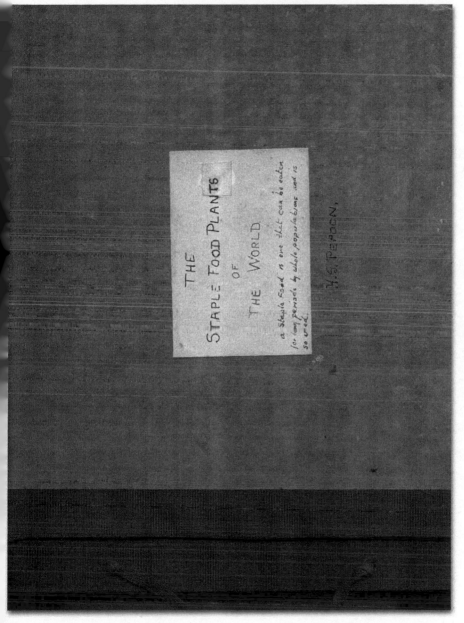

Cover for The *Staple Food Plants of the World*, showing Pepoon's diverse interest in edible plants.

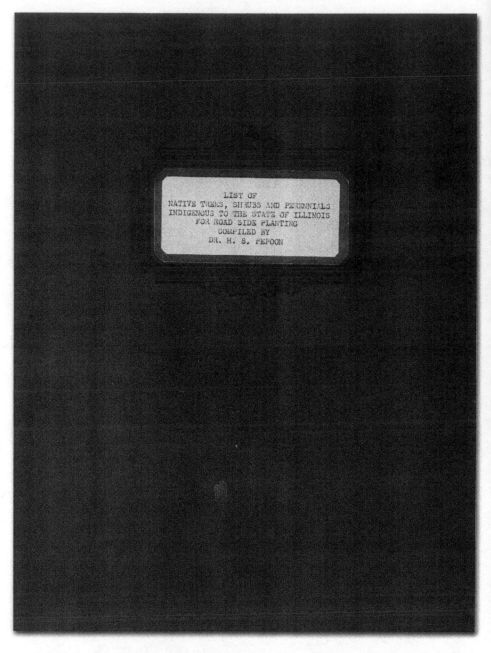

LIST OF
NATIVE TREES, SHRUBS AND PERENNIALS
INDIGENOUS TO THE STATE OF ILLINOIS
FOR ROAD SIDE PLANTING
COMPILED BY
DR. H. S. PEPOON

List of Native Trees, Shrubs and Perennials Indigenous to the State of Illinois for Roadside Planting from 1937. Pepoon being ahead of his time in this collection promoting native plants for widespread use.

WAHOO? NO, IT'S BLUE ASH AND BIGGEST KNOWN

Huge Tree Is Found at City's Edge.

"Wahoo?" asked Dr. Verne O. Graham, principal of the Norwood Park elementary school, last week.

"No," replied his companion, Herman S. Pepoon, well known botanist and former Lake View High school teacher, "looks like a blue ash."

The tree, which the two men had come upon in a trek thru the Caldwell forest preserve in search of fungi was found to be the largest blue ash in the country, and Dr. Graham, who is also president of the Illinois Academy of Sciences, has mailed an official report of the discovery to the American Forestry association in Washington.

Giant of the Forest.

This tree, just north of Devon avenue and about 50 feet west of the north branch of the river, has a circumference, four and one-half feet above the ground, of 6 feet 8 inches, Dr. Graham reported. Forestry records say the largest blue ash known is only 3 feet 1 inch in circumference and is at Piqua, O. The tree is common thruout the north central states.

Dr. Graham pointed out that the tree is peculiar in that it has a square twig, a distinction shared only with one other species of flora known as the wahoo, which is also a member of the ash family.

Really a Blue Ash.

"The tree seemed too big to be either of these," Dr. Graham said, "but we checked up on it and found that it really was a blue ash."

Science classes from the Norwood Park school already have made excursions to the tree and have made measurements revealing its height as 40 feet and its branch spread as 80 feet.

Dr. Graham lives at 4028 Grace street and Mr. Pepoon at 4927 North Tripp avenue.

Wild Flower Society.

The annual dinner meeting of the Illinois chapter, Wild Flower Preservation society, will be held at 6:30 o'clock this evening at the Cordon club. Dr. H. S. Pepoon will give an illustrated lecture. Mrs. Robert G. Work of Barrington is president of the chapter.

1940 article about the discovery, with colleague V.O. Graham, of the largest Blue Ash tree on record.

DR. H. S. PEPOON, NOTED BOTANIST, TEACHER IS DEAD

On Lake View Faculty for 38 Years.

Dr. Herman S. Pepoon, teacher and author of textbooks on botany, died last night in Augustana hospital at the age of 81. He had been ill only a week. He was one of the oldest University of Illinois graduates.

In 1930 Dr. Pepoon retired from teaching at the limit age of 70. He had then been teaching at Lake View High school for 38 years and hundreds of his friends and former pupils gathered to honor him at a dinner. Some of his first pupils were present.

Made "Botany Beautiful."

The Lake View Alumni association said of him then, "He has made botany a beautiful and popular subject to the students, some of whom are the fathers and mothers of his students today. He saw the school grow from a few rooms to the point where it was necessary to provide branches for its thousands of students. He saw the sparsely settled community of homes grow into a neighborhood of apartment buildings and business places. He is, without doubt, the most popular man on the teaching staff."

Besides being a national authority on his subject, Dr. Pepoon's home at 2842 Byron street annually attracted thousands to view his gardens.

Born in Warren, O.

The Pepoon family traced its ancestry from the Huguenots, the first of the American branch establishing themselves in Connecticut in 1630. Dr. Pepoon was born in Warren, O.

Dr. Pepoon entered the University of Illinois in 1877, and took his doctor of medicine degree at the old Hahnemann Medical school in Chicago. He practiced medicine for 11 years in Nebraska and Illinois.

He is survived by one son and one daughter, and a number of grandchildren and great-grandchildren.

DR. HERMAN S. PEPOON, FORMER WARREN RESIDENT, PASSES AWAY IN CHICAGO

Funeral services were held Monday in Chicago for the late Dr. Herman S. Pepoon, former resident of Warren, Ill., who died Friday in a Chicago hospital. He had been ill a week.

Dr. Pepoon was one of the oldest University of Illinois graduates.

In 1930 he retired from teaching at the age limit of 70. He had then been teaching at Lake View high school for 38 years and hundreds of his friends and former pupils gathered to honor him at a dinner. Some of his first pupils were present.

The Lake View Alumni association said of him then, "He has made botany a beautiful and popular subject to the students, some of whom are the fathers and mothers of his students today. He saw the school grow from a few rooms to the point where it was necessary to provide branches for its thousands of students. He saw the sparsley settled community of homes grow into a neighborhood of apartment buildings and business places. He is, without doubt, the most popular man on the teaching staff."

Besides being a national authority on his subject, Dr. Pepoon's home at 842 Byron street annually attracted thousands to view his gardens.

The Pepoon family traced its ancestry from the Huguenots, the first of the American branch establishing themselves in Connecticut in 1630. Dr. Pepoon was born in Warren, Ill. He entered the University of Illinois in 1877, and took his doctor of medicine degree at the old Hahnemann Medical school in Chicago. He practiced medicine for 11 years in Nebraska and Illinois.

He is survived by one son and one daughter, and a number of grandchildren and great-grandchildren.

Pepoon's obituaries from *The Chicago Tribune* and *The Galena Daily Gazette*.

Sunday's Tribune carried an article telling of the death of Dr. Herman S. Pepoon of Chicago. He was born and raised near Warren where many of his relatives still reside. He was one of the oldest graduates of the University of Illinois, and a writer of text-books on botany. He taught in the Lake View high school for 38 years, retiring from this position at the age of 70, eleven years ago. He always kept an active interest in Warren and community, and was one of the persons most effective in obtaining Apple River Canyon as a state park. He is survived by one son and one daughter, and a number of grandchildren and great-grandchildren.

ter, Mrs. C. A. Monnier, is reported to be improving, and is able to be up and around the house.

Mrs. Lester White spent Saturday afternoon in Freeport with her sister, Miss Marie Pierce.

The following nieces and nephews of the late Dr. H. S. Pepoon attended his funeral in Chicago on Dec. 29th: Phillip Townsend, Rockford, Maurice Townsend, Stockton, Mrs. Richard Townsend, Mrs. George Coppernoll and Mrs. Elwood Pierce. Dr. Pepoon was a brother to the late Mrs. James B. Townsend, well known here. They were children of Capt. George W. Pepoon, who in early days was superintendent of Jo Daviess county schools for eight years, and in 1888 was elected state legislator from this district.

The second is for resistance to impact, to blows such as happen when

Death reports from *The Galena Daily Gazette* and *The Warren Sentinel-Leader.*

Herman Silas Pepoon
1860-1941

To every naturalist in the Chicago area, Dr. Pepoon was a familiar character. The term character is used advisedly, for he was not just another person in a group; his very presence changed the group. He was born in Warren, Illinois, January 21, 1860, of George W. and Mary (Abbey) Pepoon, graduated from the University of Illinois with the class of 1881, and two years later graduated in medicine. In 1883 he married Alma A. Wilcox of Chicago (died 1893) and of this union were born three children—Rudolf S., Lucile (nurse, died in France), and Mrs. L. Constance Buckley. His second marriage (1900) was with Helen S. Foberg (died 1931).

Dr. Pepoon practiced as a physician in Nebraska and in Lewiston, Illinois, until September, 1892, when he became head of the department of botany at Lake View High School. Here he continued as teacher, school physician, and—greatest of all—"moulder of character" until his retirement in January, 1930. During this time more than ten thousand children came under his instruction.

He was a Life Member of The Chicago Academy of Sciences and Honorary Curator of Botany of that institution since 1930. The Academy published his classic reference book, *An Annotated Flora of the Chicago Area* (556 p.), in 1927. His other publications include *Studies of Plant Life,* 1900; *Representative Plants,* 1912; and many articles on botany, forestry, and ecology in scientific journals.

For many years he was active in the Illinois State Academy of Science as chairman of the botany section, as vice-president in 1914, and as treasurer in 1916 and 1917.

One of the major interests of his life concerned the preservation of Apple River Canyon as a state park. In this region he spent his youth and later identified and collected more than five hundred species of plants in the canyon area, among which was that most remarkable find, the dwarf Canadian primrose, *Primula mistassinica* Michx.

In his work for the Illinois Natural History Survey he traveled throughout the state collecting, recording, and cataloging the plants. His contributions will help to make possible, at some future date, the preparation of an accurate manual of the plants of Illinois.

If we measure greatness in teaching by the change brought forth in the learner, Dr. Pepoon was one of the greatest teachers this country has produced. Each of his ten thousand students has felt his influence; his buoyant spirit changed work from drudgery to joyous effort.

V. O. Graham.

Tribute to Pepoon from *Transactions of the Illinois State Academy of Science,* written by his colleague and friend V. O. Graham.

BIBLIOGRAPHY.
(Biography)

Associated Press 1931; "Giant Vines in the Smokes." 1931.

Chicago Tribune 1941. "Wahoo? No, It's Blue Ash and Biggest Known." *The Chicago Tribune,* April 20, 1941.

Domer 1997. Domer, Dennis. *Alfred Caldwell: the life and work of a prairie school landscape architect.* Baltimore, Maryland: Johns Hopkins University Press, 1997.

Eifert 1965. Eifert, Virginia S. "Primrose Watchers of Apple River." *The Living Museum,* April 1965: 381-382

Graham 1942. Graham, Verne O. "The Chronical." *Chronica Botanica VII, 6 ,* 1942: 278.

Graham 1943. Graham, Verne O. "Memoirs." *Transactions of the Illinois State Academy of Science.* 1943: 38.

Greenberg 2008. Greenberg, Joel. *Of Prairie, Woods, and Water: Two Centuries of Chicago Nature Writing.* Chicago: The University of Chicago Press, 2008.

Greenwood 1955. Greenwood, J. Grace. "Apple River Canyon State Park." *Apple River Canyon State Park.* Warren Woman's Club, 1955.

Masters 1915. Masters, Edgar Lee. *Spoon River Anthology.* The Macmillian Company, 1915.

News of Chicago Society. "Inspecting Apple River." June 19, 1921: G2.

Osborne 1932. Osborne, Georgia Lou. "Brief Biographies of the Figurines on display in the Illinois State Historical Library." *American Libraries.* 1932. http://www.archive.org/stream/briefbiographies00osbo/briefbiographies00osbo_djvu.txt (accessed December 2010).

Partridge 1887. Partridge, Charles A. *History of the 96th Regiment, Illinois Volunteer Infantry.* Chicago, IL: Brown, Pettibone and Co., 1887.

Pepoon 1914. Pepoon, George Whitfield. "George Whitfield Pepoon Notes Written by Himself." 1914. Galena Public Library Historical Collections Room, Galena Illinois: Accessed 12/10/2010.

Pepoon 1940. Pepoon, H.S. "Halfhours of Living." *Nature Notes - The Magazine of Outdoor Information, Volume VII, Number 5*, May 1940: 125.

Saylor 2010. Saylor, Douglas. "Mary Pepoon Howe: Writer and Suffragist in Pioneer Nebraska." *Associated Content.* September 7, 2010. http://www.associatedcontent.com/article/5754656/mary_pepoon_howe_writer_and_suffragist.html?cat=37 (accessed December 2010).

Smith 1971. Smith, Wilbur M. *Before I Forget.* Chicago Il: Moody Press, 1971.

Stupka 1976. Stupka, Arthur. "Trees, Shrubs, and Woody Vines of Great Smoky Mountains National Park," 11.

Telegraph Herald 1938. *Woman's Club to Meet.* "Telegraph Herald." April 25, 1938.

The Chicago Tribune 1941. "Dr. H.S. Pepoon, Noted Botanist, Teacher is Dead" *The Chicago Tribune,* December 27, 1941: 12.

University of Illinois 1918. *The semi-centennial alumni record of the University of Illinois.* Chicago: R.R. Donnelley, 1918.

Unknown 1930. "The Warren High-School Literary Society." *The Warren High-School Literary Society also Names of Some of Miss Fields Students,* 26-28. 1930.

War Department 1946. *Illinois World War II Casualties Army and Air Force.* U. S. War Department, 1946.

Whitman 1930. Whitman, Jay M. "The Pepoon Family Biographical Sketch." *The Warren Sentinel-Leader,* July 9, 1930: 41-45.

(Essays)

Pepoon, H.S. "A Proposed New State Park." *Transactions of the Illinois State Academy of Science.* Illinois State Academy of Science, 1919. 64-68.

Pepoon, H.S. "An Ecological Survey of the Driftless Area (Part 1)." *School of Science and Mathmatics* (Illinois State Academy of Science) 9 (1909): 441-446.

Pepoon, H.S. "An Ecological Survey of the Driftless Area (Part 2)." *School of Science and Mathmatics* (Illinois State Academy of Science) 9 (1909): 522-527.

—. "Cliff Flora of Jo Daviess County." *Transactions of the Illinois State Academy of Science.* Illinois State Academy of Science, 1909. 32-37.

—. "Peculiar Examples of Plant Distribution." *Transactions of the Illinois State Academy of Science.* Illinois State Academy of Science, 1916. 128-137.

Pepoon, H.S. "Primula mistassinica in Illinois and in Distribution." Illinois Natural History Survey, Urbana, Illinois, 1933, 1-6. Box Number 15, Folder number 1, Herman Silas Pepoon Papers, Chicago Academy of Sciences.

Pepoon, H.S. "The Apple River Canyon of Jo Daviess County - A Proposed State Park," *Proposed Park Areas in the State of Illinois - A Report with Recomendations.* The Friends of our Native Landscape, Chicago, IL, 1921. 17-23.

—. "The Flora of the Right of Way of the Illinois Central Railway: Waddams to East Dubuque." *Transactions of the Illinois State Academy of Science.* Illinois State Academy of Science, 1927. 92-100.

—. "The Forest Associations of Northwest Illinois." *Transactions of the Illinois State Academy of Science.* Illinois State Academy of Science, 1910. 143-156.

—. "The Forest Lands of Jo Daviess County." *Transactions of the Illinois State Academy of Science.* Illinois State Academy of Science, 1919. 183-202.

—. "Destruction of a Farm Flora." *The Plant World, an Illustrated Monthly Journal of Popular Botany and Official Organ of The Wildflower Preservation Society of America,* 1904: 43-45.

—. "The Primrose Rocks of Illinois." *Transactions of the Illinois Academy of Science.* Illinois State Academy of Science, 1917. 159-162.

(Scrapbook Images)

Page 127: Picture of Warren Academy: The Warren High-School Literary Society Winter of 1876-1877, History Room, Warren Township Library, Warren Illinois. Accessed 12/14/2010.

Page 127: Herm Pepoon Poems: The Warren High-School Literary Society Winter of 1876-1877, History Room, Warren Township Library, Warren Illinois. Accessed 12/14/2010.

Page 127: *The Deserted Village*: The Warren High-School Literary Society Winter of 1876-1877, History Room, Warren Township Library, Warren Illinois. Accessed 12/14/2010.

Page 128: Frink and Walker Stagecoach Drawing: Apple River Canyon State Park File, Galena Public Library Historical Collections Room, Galena Illinois: Accessed 12/9/2010.

Page 129: "Plants to be Named" (Newspaper Clipping) *American Bee Journal,* September 24, 1896, page 618.

Page 130: "Explosion in Laboratory Injures High School Girl" (Newspaper Clipping), *Chicago Tribune*; March 15, 1902, page 1.

Page 131: Home Farm Species List: Box Number, 8, Herman Silas Pepoon Papers, Chicago Academy of Sciences.

Page 132: *The Three Botanists* Photo: Box Number, 1, Herman Silas Pepoon Papers, Chicago Academy of Sciences.

Page 133: Picture "Herman S. Pepoon M.D. The Poet of 1876-1877:" The Warren High-School Literary Society Winter of 1876-1877, History Room, Warren Township Library, Warren Illinois. Accessed 12/14/2010.

Page 134: Travel Drawing of Twenty Collecting Trips Jo Daviess County 1919: Box Number, 5, Herman Silas Pepoon Papers, Chicago Academy of Sciences.

Page 135: "Tablet Honors War Nurse Who Gave Her Life" (Newspaper Clipping), *Chicago Tribune* May 30, 1921, Page 10.

Page 135: "Wild Flower Society" (Newspaper Clipping), *Chicago Tribune*, April 21, 1934, page 21.

Page 135: "Prairie Club Hike" (Newspaper Clipping), *Chicago Tribune*, June 3, 1916, page 14.

Page 136: Jo Daviess County Plant Collection Trips 1919: Box Number, 5, Herman Silas Pepoon Papers, Chicago Academy of Sciences.

Page 137: The Fruits of the Chicago Market (Cover): Box Number, 3, Herman Silas Pepoon Papers, Chicago Academy of Sciences.

Page 138: "Woods and Waters" (Newspaper Clipping), *Chicago Tribune*, December 19, 1921, page 18.

Page 139: Sketch Map of N. W. Illinois: Box Number, 1, Herman Silas Pepoon Papers, Chicago Academy of Sciences.

Page: 140: Line Drawing of Clear Creek Valley Drainage Basin: Box Number, 5, Herman Silas Pepoon Papers, Chicago Academy of Sciences.

Page 141: Line Drawing Showing Influence of Topography on Plant Distribution: Box Number, 5, Herman Silas Pepoon Papers, Chicago Academy of Sciences.

Page 142: Unique Flower Locations for Jo Daviess County: Box Number, 5, Herman Silas Pepoon Papers, Chicago Academy of Sciences.

Page 143: Line Drawing of Stephenson County: Box Number, 3, Herman Silas Pepoon Papers, Chicago Academy of Sciences.

Page 144: Three Photos of Apple River Canyon and Powers Mound: Photo Box Number 1, Herman Silas Pepoon Papers, Chicago Academy of Sciences.

Page 145: Line Drawing of the Topography of Apple River Canyon: Box Number 5, Herman Silas Pepoon Papers, Chicago Academy of Sciences.

Page 146: "Inspecting Apple River" (Newspaper Clipping), *Chicago Tribune*; June 19, 1921, page G2.

Page 146: "Society to Preserve Wild Flowers Meets" (Newspaper Clipping), *Chicago Tribune,* December 19, 1921, page 23.

Page 147: Prairie Club Outing Photos at Apple River: Box Number, 5, Herman Silas Pepoon Papers, Chicago Academy of Sciences.

Page 148: Photos of Primrose Cliffs: Photo Box Number, 1, Herman Silas Pepoon Papers, Chicago Academy of Sciences.

Page 149: Postcard of Pitcher Plant: Authors Collection

Page 150: Book Cover, *Flora of the Chicago Region*: Authors Collection

Page 151: Book Title Page, *Flora of the Chicago Region*: Authors Collection

Page 152: Revised List of Plants of Jo Daviess County: Box Number, 4, Herman Silas Pepoon Papers, Chicago Academy of Sciences.

Page 153: Picture Lake View High School: Uptown Chicago History. http://uptownhistory.compassrose.org/2008/04/lake-view-high-school-ashland-and.html (accessed December 2010).

Page 154: "Goodbye and Good Luck" (Newspaper Clipping), *Chicago Herald Examiner*, January 22, 1930. Warren History Folder, Galena Public Library Historical Collections Room, Galena Illinois: Accessed 12/9/2010.

Page 154: "Tells How Beds of Lotus Sprang Up Over Illinois" (Newspaper Clipping), *Chicago Tribune*; October 20, 1933, page 7.

Page 155: "Pepoon, Barrett Make Plant Study in Chicago" (Newspaper Clipping),

Bibliography

Daily Illini; January 10, 1932.

Page 156: Line Drawing of Sulpher Cinquefoil: Box Number, 12, Herman Silas Pepoon Papers, Chicago Academy of Sciences.

Page 157: Line Drawing of Fern Species: Box Number, 12, Herman Silas Pepoon Papers, Chicago Academy of Sciences.

Page 158: Line Drawing of Yellow Perch: Box Number, 12, Herman Silas Pepoon Papers, Chicago Academy of Sciences.

Page 159: The Staple Food Plants of the World Cover: Box Number, 14, Herman Silas Pepoon Papers, Chicago Academy of Sciences.

Page 160: List of Native Trees and Shrubs and Perennials for Illinois Roadside Planting Cover: Box Number, 2, Herman Silas Pepoon Papers, Chicago Academy of Sciences.

Page 161: "Wahoo? No It's Blue Ash and Biggest Known" (Newspaper Clipping), *Chicago Tribune*; April 20, 1941, page nw2.

Page 155: "Wild Flower Society" (Newspaper Clipping), *Chicago Tribune* March 27, 1940, page 19.

Page 162: Obituary "Dr. Herman S. Pepoon, Former Warren Resident, Passes Away in Chicago:" Galena Daily Gazette, December 30 1941, Galena Public Library Historical Collections Room, Galena Illinois: Accessed 12/10/2010.

Page 162: Obituary "Dr. H.S. Pepoon, Noted Botanist, Teacher is Dead" *Chicago Tribune*, December 27, 1941, page 12.

Page 163: Clip about Pepoon's Death: *Galena Daily Gazette-* Warren News, January 3 1942, Galena Public Library Historical Collections Room, Galena Illinois: Accessed 12/10/2010.

Page 163: News about Pepoon's Funeral: The Warren Sentinel-Leader January 3, 1942. History Room, Warren Township Library, Warren Illinois. Accessed 12/14/2010.

Page 164: "Herman Silas Pepoon 1860-1941" Transactions of the Illinois State Academy of Science. *Memoirs*, 1943: 38.

GLOSSARY.

Alluvial: Loose, unconsolidated (not cemented together into a solid rock), soil or sediments, eroded, deposited, and reshaped by water in some form in a non-marine setting

Amelioration: The act of making better, to improve; to heal; to solve a problem.

Amanita: A poisonous mushroom.

Bailey: In reference to the work of Loring Woart Bailey (1839-1925), American educator, botanist and author.

Boreal: Of or relating to the north climates; northern.

Britton: Short for the botanical reference book by Nathanial Lord Britton (1859-1934), *Illustrated Flora of the Northern United States, Canada, and the British Possessions* (1896).

Castellated: having or resembling repeated square indentations.

Chert: A variety of silica that contains microcrystalline quartz. Often found on the soil surface.

Elysian: Of, relating to, or characteristic of heaven or paradise.

Galena Junction, Illinois: Railroad place name, located on the south side of the Galena River where it meets the Mississippi.

Galena Limestone: The upper most layer of limestone rock and the softest of limestones. It is the prevailing surface rock in the Lead Region.

Gray: Short for the botanical reference book by Asa Gray (1810-1888), *Manual of the Botany of the Northern United States, from New England to Wisconsin and South to Ohio and Pennsylvania Inclusive* (1848).

Hydrarch: Having originated in a wet habitat.

Loess: Sediment formed by the accumulation of wind-blown silt and lesser amounts of sand and clay that are loosely cemented by calcium carbonate.

Michaux: In reference to Andre Michaux (1746-1802) French botanist and explorer who named *Primula mistassinica* (Canadian Primrose, Rock Primrose, Bird's Eye Primrose). The credited name often cited as *Primula mistassinica* Michx.

Millville: A former stagecoach town located where Apple Canyon State Park's parking lot and pavilions now sit. It was in continual decline since the 1850's and washed away in a flood in 1892.

Niagara Limestone: General term identifying the limestone of the Niagara Escarpment, a long escarpment (a steep slope or long cliff resulting from erosion or faulting and separating two relatively level areas of differing elevations) that runs westward from New York through Ontario, Michigan, Wisconsin and Illinois. It is the namesake of Niagara Falls.

Platteville Limestone: The layer of limestone found beneath Galena limestone, distinguished by its hardness.

Portage, Illinois: Railroad place name located on the north side of the Galena River where it meets the Mississippi.

Protoplasmic: Relating to protoplasm, the living content of cells within plants.

Rod: A unit of measure equaling 5½ yards or 16½ feet.

Sic: generally inside square brackets, [sic], indicates that the passage is just as it appears from its original source. Derived from the Latin adverb sic meaning "intentionally so written."

Talus: An accumulation of broken rock fragments at the base of cliffs or valley shoulders. Landforms associated with these materials are sometimes called talus piles.

Vale: A valley, often containing a stream.

Viz: Abbreviation for videlicet, used to introduce examples and details.

Waddams, Illinois: Known today as Waddams Grove, located Between Lena and Nora, Illinois. It was the first settlement in Stephenson County.

Wallace: John Findlay Wallace, manager of the Illinois Central Railroad 1891-1904; he went on to engineer the Panama Canal.

Xerophytic: Plants that are adapted to growing in dry conditions.

INDICES.
(Biography)

Indices

(H.S. Pepoon Essays)

42 Degrees Latitude 38

A.